Materials for the "Say YES to Youth"
Project were funded by a grant
from the Carnegie Foundation to
Detroit Public Library.

APR 0 6 2006   HU

BIOMES

OF THE WORLD

VOLUME 4
Wetlands

MICHAEL ALLABY

GROLIER
EDUCATIONAL

About This Set

Biomes of the World is a nine-volume set that describes all the major landscapes (biomes) that are found across the Earth. Biomes are large areas of the world where living conditions for plants and animals are broadly similar, so that the vegetation in these locations appears much the same. Each of the books in this set describes one or more of the main biomes: Volume 1: The Polar Regions (tundra, ice cap, and permanent ice); Volume 2: Deserts (desert and semidesert); Volume 3: Oceans (oceans and islands); **Volume 4: Wetlands** (lakes, rivers, marshes, and estuaries); Volume 5: Mountains (mountain and highland); Volume 6: Temperate Forests (boreal coniferous forest or taiga, coastal coniferous forest, broad-leaf and mixed forest, Mediterranean forest and scrub); Volume 7: Tropical Forests (rain forest and monsoon forest); Volume 8: Temperate Grasslands (prairie, steppe, and pampas); Volume 9: Tropical Grasslands (savanna).

The books each have three sections. The first describes the geographical location of the biome, its climate, and other physical features that make it the way it is. The second section describes the plants and animals that inhabit the biome and the ways in which they react to each other. The final section of each book deals with the threats to the biome and what is being done to reduce these. An introduction in Volume 1 includes a map showing all the biomes described in this set, and a map showing all the countries of the world.

Throughout the pages of this set there are diagrams explaining the processes described in the text, artwork depictions of animals and plants, diagrams showing ecosystems, and tables. The many color photographs bring each biome to life. At the end of each book there is a glossary explaining the meaning of technical words used, a list of other sources of reference (books and websites), followed by an index to all the volumes in the set.

Published 1999 by Grolier Educational,
Danbury, CT 06816

This edition published exclusively for the school and library market

Planned and produced by
Andromeda Oxford Limited,
11–13 The Vineyard, Abingdon, Oxon
OX14 3PX, UK

Copyright © Andromeda Oxford Limited 1999

Project Manager: *Graham Bateman*
Editors: *Jo Newson, Penelope Isaac*
Art Editor and Designer: *Steve McCurdy*
Cartography: *Richard Watts, Tim Williams*
Editorial Assistant: *Marian Dreier*
Picture Manager: *Claire Turner*
Production: *Nicolette Colborne*

Origination by Expo Holdings Sdn Bhd, Malaysia
Printed in Hong Kong

Set ISBN 0-7172-9341-6
Volume 4 ISBN 0-7172-9345-9

Biomes of the world.
    p.   cm.
    Includes indexes.
    Contents: v. 1. Polar regions -- v. 2. Deserts -- v. 3. Oceans -- v. 4. Wetlands -- v. 5. Mountains -- v. 6. Temperate forests -- v. 7. Tropical forests -- v. 8. Temperate grassland -- v. 9. Tropical grassland.
    Summary: In nine volumes, explores each of the earth's major ecological regions, defining important features, animals, and environmental issues.
    ISBN 0-7172-9341-6 (hardcover : set : alk. paper). -- ISBN 0-7172-9345-9 (hardcover : vol. 4 : alk. paper)
    1. Biotic communities--juvenile literature. 2. Life zones--Juvenile literature. 3. Ecology--Juvenile literature. [1. Biotic communities.] I. Grolier Educational (Firm)
QH541.14.B57   1999
577--dc21   98-37524
                                              CIP
                                               AC

Contents

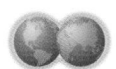

The Physical World of Wetlands

*W*here a large river meets the sea, low tides often expose large expanses of mud and sand. Flat and featureless, these sandbanks and mudflats look uninteresting. It is not long after the tide has receded, however, that visitors start to arrive. Birds of many species alight on the surface to feed on the rich communities of bacteria and invertebrate animals living below the surface.

Wetlands are areas of wet ground that are covered by water permanently or at certain times. They include marshes, bogs, swamps, and fens, and they are often found around rivers, lakes, and streams.

Wetlands also occur along coasts and in estuaries, and they include deltas. Estuaries are formed where a river meets the sea, and the delta is the flat area of deposited silt where the mainstream splits into smaller branches. Very large rivers, such as the Nile in Africa, the Ganges in India and Bangladesh, the Mekong in Southeast Asia, and the Mississippi in the United States, form deltas covering vast areas.

Farther inland, upstream of the point in the river reached by the tides, there is another type of wetland area, the river floodplain—almost level land across which the river meanders slowly. The floodplain is covered with a layer of fine soil, rich in plant nutrients, deposited when the river overflowed its banks or changed its course. It is fertile ground. Farming settlements often grow up on floodplains, but they are not safe places to live, as they are vulnerable to flooding.

On low ground part of the floodplain may be covered with shallow water for part of the year. This soft, wet ground is called a marsh. Marshes are found by the edges of some lakes, rivers, and streams. They support many plants such as sedges, cattails, and rushes. These plants grow rooted in the mud but with their leaves above the surface.

Wet, spongy ground containing decaying vegetation is called a bog. In temperate and cold regions decaying vegetation takes the form of peat—a dark brown deposit. Peat bogs are

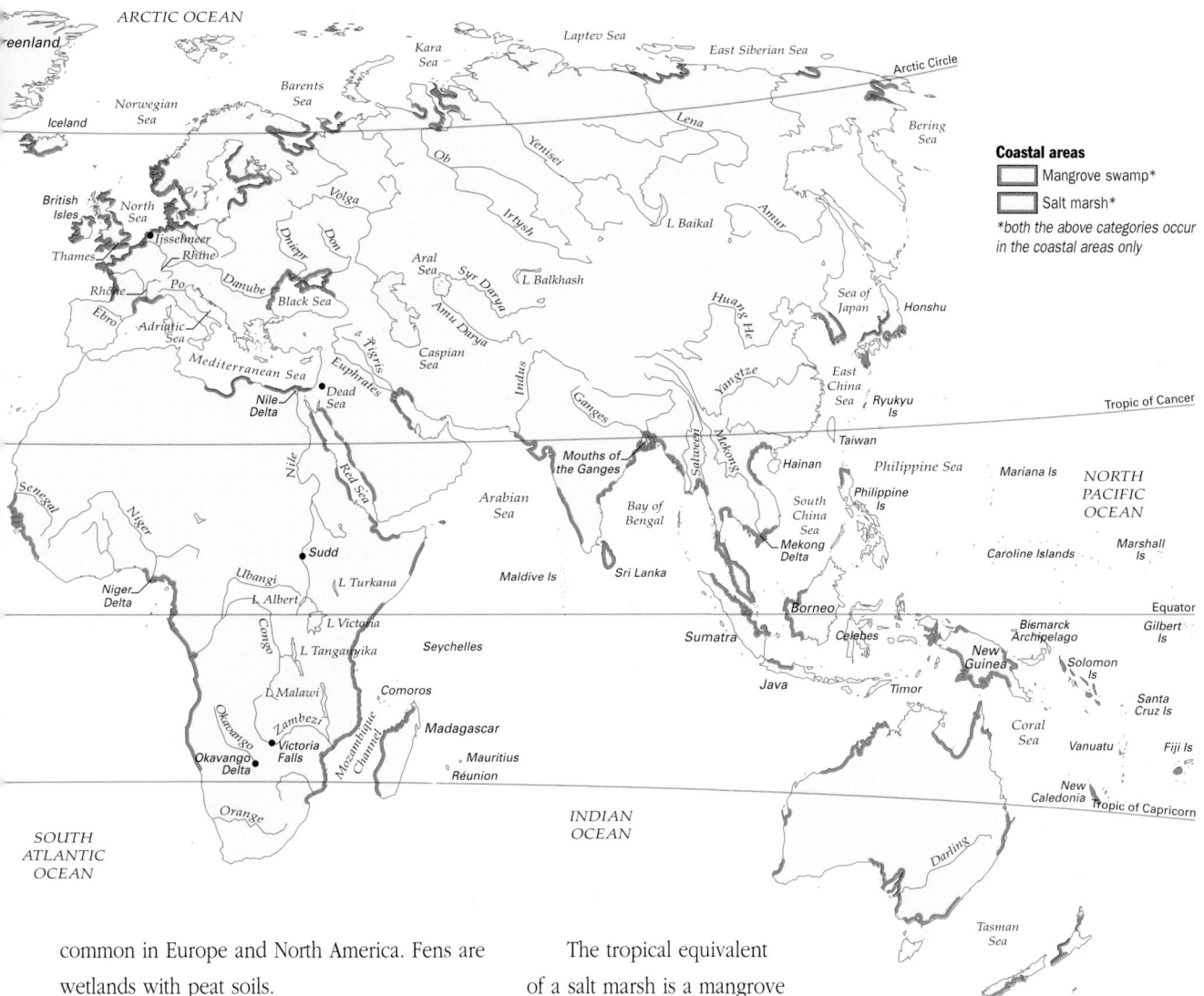

common in Europe and North America. Fens are wetlands with peat soils.

Nearer to the equator there are low-lying areas that are covered with shallow water for much of the year or in some cases all the time. These are swamps. Unlike the marshes found in higher latitudes they contain bigger plants, including shrubs and trees. Some swamps support forests of trees that are adapted to the wet conditions.

Swamps and marshes occur in fresh water. In high latitudes wetlands along coasts and in river estuaries and deltas develop as salt marshes—flat areas of marshy ground that are inundated with salt water with the tides.

The tropical equivalent of a salt marsh is a mangrove swamp; mangrove trees can grow in the salty, airless ground.

Wetlands contain plants that are valuable to people. Common reeds are still used for making thatched roofs, and various species of willow are collected to make baskets and other wicker items. In some marshes in Iraq and Africa papyrus is harvested and used to make boats. It was once the raw material for making paper. Peat makes a good soil conditioner and is used in some countries as a fuel. Above all, however, wetlands are important for migrating birds and the other wildlife that inhabits them.

WETLANDS are found all over the world and are not limited to specific climatic conditions. They occur beside the lower reaches of giant rivers. River delta wetlands include those of the Nile in Africa and the Mississippi in the United States. The map also shows areas where salt marshes and mangrove swamps occur.

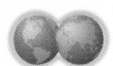
LAND AND WATER

THE HYDROLOGICAL CYCLE. Water evaporates from any exposed surface, including lakes, rivers, and oceans. Plants take water from the soil and release it (transpiration). Water vapor condenses to form clouds, then falls as precipitation. Some of the precipitation evaporates, and some is taken up by plants; the remainder drains down through the soil to form groundwater, which flows into rivers and eventually back to the sea.

Water drains from the land and collects in rivers, which flow to the sea. Plants take water from the soil and move it to their leaves, where it is released (in a process called transpiration) and evaporates. Water also evaporates from the sea and land. It returns as precipitation (rain, snow, hail, or fog). This is the hydrological cycle. All life on land depends on it. It is possible because of certain remarkable properties of water.

Water can exist in three states—as a gas, as a liquid, and as a solid—at ordinary temperatures (those usually experienced at the Earth's surface). In winter it is quite common to find a pond with ice around its edge and a small amount of mist above the surface. The open pond is liquid, the

ice is solid, and the mist is composed of droplets that have condensed from water vapor (water in its gaseous form).

A water molecule consists of two atoms of hydrogen (H) and one of oxygen (O). The formula is usually written as H_2O, but it can also be written as H–O–H. There is a negative electric charge on the oxygen atom, and a positive charge on the hydrogen atoms, and the attraction between the negative and positive atoms holds the molecule together.

The two hydrogen atoms are both on the same side of the oxygen atom. Because of this the hydrogen side of the molecule carries a small positive charge, and the oxygen side a small negative charge. Molecules that carry no overall charge (they are neutral) but have small opposite charges at their ends, or "poles," are called polar

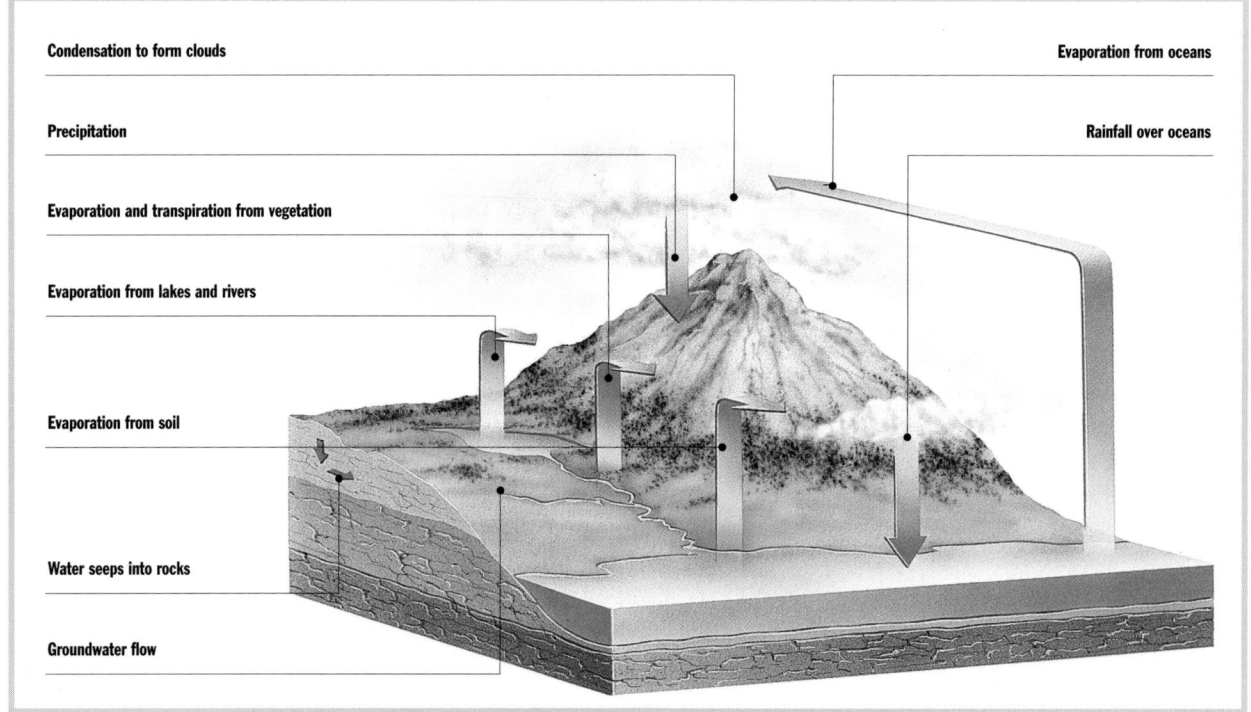

Condensation to form clouds

Precipitation

Evaporation and transpiration from vegetation

Evaporation from lakes and rivers

Evaporation from soil

Water seeps into rocks

Groundwater flow

Evaporation from oceans

Rainfall over oceans

molecules. In the case of water the hydrogen side of the molecule can form a weak attachment—a hydrogen bond—with the oxygen side of an adjacent water molecule.

Evaporation and Condensation

While water is in its liquid form, hydrogen bonds hold small groups of water molecules together. The groups can move around and slide past each other; this allows water to flow. When the water is warmed, the molecules absorb heat energy. This makes them move faster, and they try to pull free from their groups. Eventually, they have enough energy to break free. At the surface of the water single molecules are able to escape into the air. This is evaporation, and the escaped

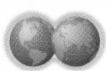

MAJOR RIVERS OF THE WORLD

River	Length		Discharge		Flowing into
	miles	km	cubic feet/sec	cu. m/sec	
Nile	4,157	6,689	90,000	2,547	Mediterranean Sea
Amazon	4,000	6,436	4,200,000	118,860	Atlantic Ocean
Yangtze	3,434	5,525	770,000	21,791	East China Sea
Huang He	2,901	4,666	116,000	3,283	Yellow Sea
Paraná	2,796	4,499	550,000	15,565	Atlantic Ocean
Lena	2,650	4,264	530,000	14,999	Arctic Ocean
Mackenzie	2,635	4,240	450,000	12,735	Arctic Ocean
Congo	2,716	4,370	1,400,000	39,620	Atlantic Ocean
Niger	2,600	4,183	250,000	7,075	Gulf of Guinea
Yenisei	2,566	4,129	614,000	17,376	Arctic Ocean
Mekong	2,500	4,022	600,000	16,980	South China Sea
Missouri	2,466	3,968	64,000	1,811	Mississippi River
Mississippi	2,348	3,778	620,000	17,546	Gulf of Mexico
Ob	2,287	3,680	441,000	12,480	Arctic Ocean
Volga	2,292	3,688	286,000	8,094	Caspian Sea
Madeira	2,013	3,239	600,000	16,980	Amazon River

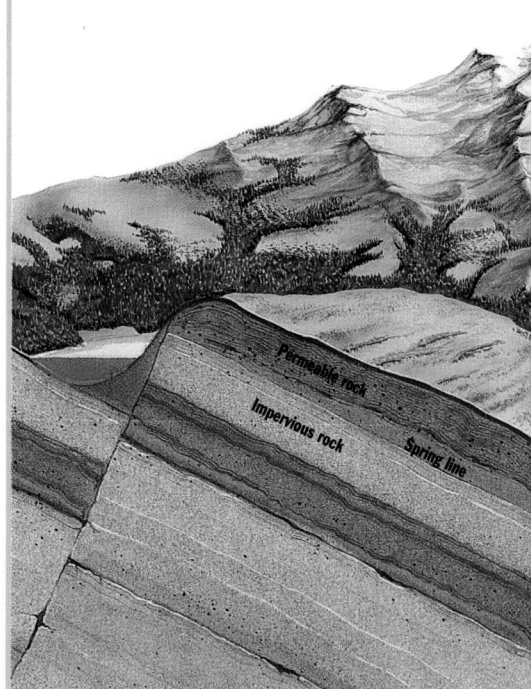

ROUTES TO THE SEA. Rainwater falling on the land follows many routes to the sea. Where the surface of the rock is impervious, the water runs off to form ponds or to join rivers. Where the rock is permeable, water seeps through it until it reaches an impervious layer. It then flows along the surface of this rock layer until it emerges on the ground.

molecules then exist as a gas—water vapor.

If the air is cooled, the water molecules lose energy. This makes them move more slowly. Eventually, they collide with the surface of a tiny solid particle, the hydrogen bonds reform, and they become very small droplets of water. This process is called condensation.

The temperature at which water evaporates and condenses is called the dew point temperature. It is the temperature at which the air is saturated—it can hold no more water vapor. The warmer the air, the more water vapor it can contain, but, as the air cools, the amount of water vapor decreases.

Airborne water droplets form clouds, and within clouds droplets meet and coalesce (fuse). The droplets may grow so large they fall as rain. Vertical air currents inside most clouds carry droplets high enough for them to freeze. In temperate latitudes, even in summer, the rain that falls is, in fact, melted snow.

STREAMS AND RIVERS

When water evaporates, any substances dissolved in it are left behind. Seawater contains dissolved salts, mainly sodium chloride, or common salt.

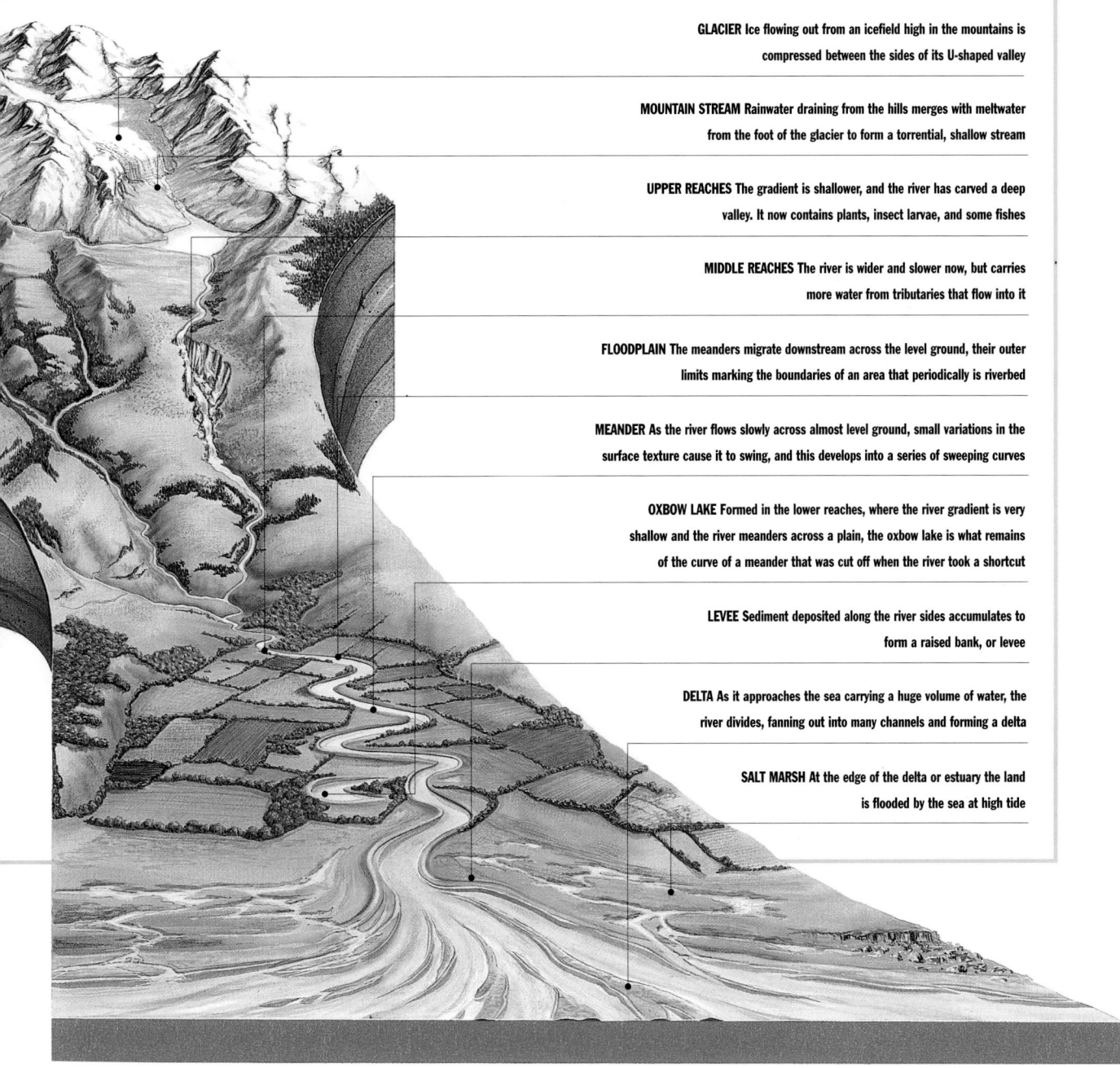

GLACIER Ice flowing out from an icefield high in the mountains is compressed between the sides of its U-shaped valley

MOUNTAIN STREAM Rainwater draining from the hills merges with meltwater from the foot of the glacier to form a torrential, shallow stream

UPPER REACHES The gradient is shallower, and the river has carved a deep valley. It now contains plants, insect larvae, and some fishes

MIDDLE REACHES The river is wider and slower now, but carries more water from tributaries that flow into it

FLOODPLAIN The meanders migrate downstream across the level ground, their outer limits marking the boundaries of an area that periodically is riverbed

MEANDER As the river flows slowly across almost level ground, small variations in the surface texture cause it to swing, and this develops into a series of sweeping curves

OXBOW LAKE Formed in the lower reaches, where the river gradient is very shallow and the river meanders across a plain, the oxbow lake is what remains of the curve of a meander that was cut off when the river took a shortcut

LEVEE Sediment deposited along the river sides accumulates to form a raised bank, or levee

DELTA As it approaches the sea carrying a huge volume of water, the river divides, fanning out into many channels and forming a delta

SALT MARSH At the edge of the delta or estuary the land is flooded by the sea at high tide

On land rain and melted snow soak down through the soil until the water meets a layer of impervious, or impenetrable, rock or clay. It flows downhill, moving very slowly. At this stage it is called groundwater; the upper limit of the saturated soil is called the water table.

Where the line of the impervious layer comes close to the surface of the land, water flows over the ground, either slowly seeping out or flowing vigorously from a spring. It continues over the surface, running downhill as a stream.

DELTA TYPES. Deltas are of several distinct types, the variations being due to differences in the currents and tides influencing their formation. The Mississippi (1) has a birdfoot delta. The Nile (2) has an arcuate delta. The Mekong (3) has a tidal delta, and the Niger (4) has a combined delta.

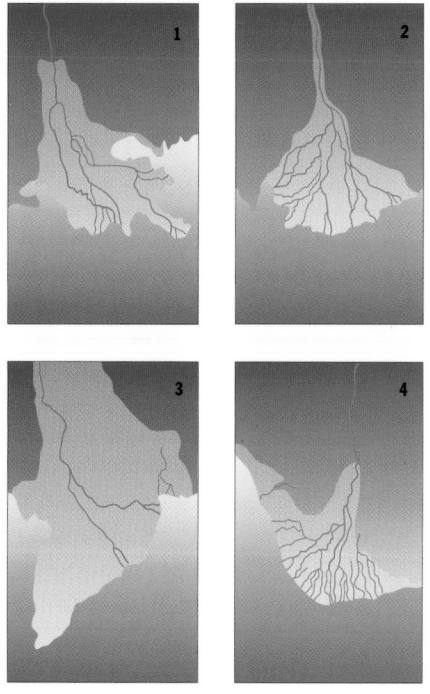

Many streams grow into rivers that join larger rivers as tributaries. Rivers that flow all the way to the sea change in character several times.

River Zones

These changes mark the boundaries of zones, or reaches, into which a river can be divided for purposes of study (although any particular river may lack one or more of these zones). The zones differ in the temperature of the water, which becomes warmer the farther it is from the source; the speed with which the river flows; and the amount of sediment the water carries. These differences are reflected in the different species of plants and animals living in each zone. One method of classifying river zones divides the river into four sections.

The first zone occurs near the river's source. Here, the river is small, but flows rapidly. The amount of water it carries varies with the seasons

AN INLAND DELTA. The Okavango River drains into a basin in the Kalahari Desert of South Africa. Thick masses of papyrus reeds grow up to block river channels, forcing them to change direction.

and the amount of rainfall present. The temperature of the water also varies, and the river may contain no fish. This is called the headstream or highland brook.

A little lower, the river is bigger, and its flow more constant. If its bed is rocky, the river may still flow as a torrent. A very few fish may be present, usually trout or salmon. This section of the river is known as the trout beck.

Farther downstream the river has begun to collect silt and other soil particles washed into it from the land to either side. The water still flows swiftly, but there are hollows among the rocks on the bed where sediment collects. Plants can grow in the water, and there are more species of fish. This is called the minnow reach or grayling zone.

Finally, the river crosses a low-lying plain as it approaches the sea. It is large, but it flows slowly and meanders. This section is the lowland reach—in Europe it is sometimes called the bream zone.

DELTAS

A river carries plant and animal remains and soil particles that it has gathered along its course. This accumulation of solid material is carried to the river mouth, where some is deposited as sediment; the remainder is carried away by the tides and currents. The amount carried by a major river can be very large. The Amazon in South America, for example, delivers almost 500 million tons (454 million t) of sediment to the ocean every year, the Ganges in India about 1,600 million tons (1,453 million t), and the Mississippi in the United States carries 213 million tons (193 million t). Tides and ocean currents cannot remove sediment as fast as these great rivers deliver it. The result is a delta.

It was the Greek historian Herodotus who coined the term "delta" in about 490 B.C. He noticed that where the Nile flows into the Mediterranean Sea, it divides into many separate channels that fan out to make a triangular shape. To Greeks approaching by sea from the north, the shape resembled the capital of the fourth letter in the Greek alphabet, delta (Δ). Instead of the sediment disappearing into the open sea, it was deposited. The river then had to cut channels through it, which resulted in it dividing into separate channels.

Deltas are shaped by the river and by the action of waves and tides, any one of which may be dominant. The Mekong and Ganges have tidal deltas, dominated by tidal flow.

The Mississippi delta is different. Its formation is dominated by the river, which has changed its course several times during the last

THE HUANG HE, or Yellow River, in China, once flowed southeast from Zhenzhou, but in 1861 it changed course and now flows into the Gulf of Chihli. The entire plain is vulnerable to flooding. In 1933 the waters rose by 100 feet (30 m) in some areas; in 1938 a deliberate breaching of the south dike caused the death by drowning of up to 900,000 people.

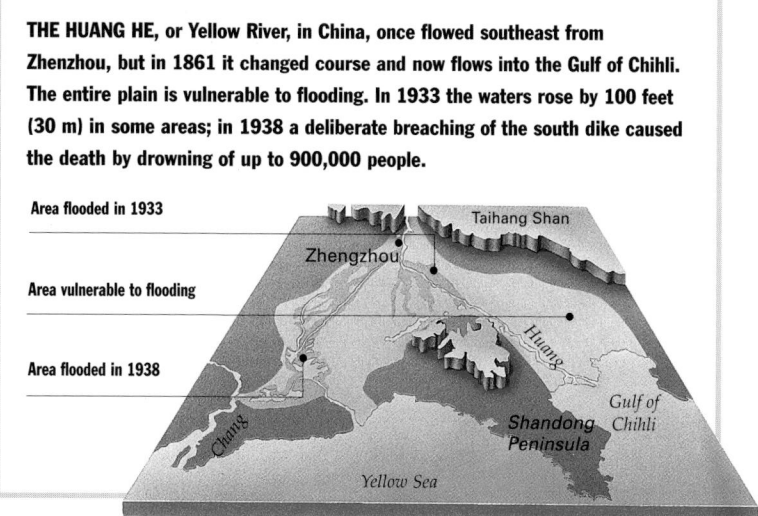

Area flooded in 1933

Area vulnerable to flooding

Area flooded in 1938

Taihang Shan

Zhengzhou

Huang

Gulf of Chihli

Shandong Peninsula

Chang

Yellow Sea

7,000 years or so. This has produced seven overlapping deltas, resulting in a shape resembling a bird's foot or claw. This type of delta is called a birdfoot delta. The intricate pattern of the Niger delta in West Africa is produced by a combination of all three forces.

LAKES

Water flowing into a natural depression will fill it, forming a lake. Lakes can be enormous. The Great Lakes of North America—Ontario, Erie, Huron, Michigan, and Superior—cover an area of 244,108 square miles (632,239 sq. km).

These lakes formed the way many lakes form. At one time wide river valleys crossed the area the lakes now occupy. During the last ice age (which ended about 10,000 years ago) glaciers flowed into those valleys, widening and deepening them. As the ice age ended and the glaciers retreated northward, the deep basins filled with water from the melting ice. Ice sheets and glaciers scoured out many of the smaller hollows in mountain ranges that are now mountain lakes.

Not all mountain lakes are small, however. Lake Titicaca, in the Andes of South America, has a surface area of 3,200 square miles (8,288 sq. m). It is one of the highest lakes in the world, with an elevation of 12,500 feet (3,800 m) above sea level.

Lakes are fed by the water draining into them or carried into them by rivers. Most lakes lose water through one or more outflow rivers—but not all. Tarns are upland lakes out of which no river flows. This makes them mysterious

places. Local legends often suppose them to be bottomless. In fact, most tarns are relatively shallow. They lose enough water by evaporation from the surface to avoid overflowing.

Ponds are much smaller than lakes. They usually form on lower ground and have often been made to store water for farm livestock.

The Life of a Lake

Lakes age, just like living organisms, and

BANFF NATIONAL PARK *(above)* **in the Canadian Rockies has many lakes like this one, formed in depressions scoured by ice long ago, when the climate was colder.**

eventually they disappear. At first they contain water that has recently flowed into a basin. The water contains only very small amounts of the chemical compounds that nourish plants. Few plants can grow around the edges of the lake or floating near its center, so there are very few invertebrate animals or fish. The water is clear and clean. A lake at this stage in its life cycle, which is poor in nutrients and plant life, is called oligotrophic, from the Greek *oligos*, meaning "small," and *trophe*, meaning "nourishment."

Water draining into the lake from the surrounding land brings plant nutrients that dissolved into it as it flowed through the soil. As the nutrients accumulate in the lake, more and more plants are able to grow in it, and more animals arrive to feed on the plants. The lake is now "middle-aged" and has an intermediate amount of nutrients. It is said to be mesotrophic (the Greek word for middle is *mesos*).

Nutrients continue to drain into the lake, and the plant life becomes more abundant. As plants shed leaves and die, organic matter accumulates on the lake bed. Little by little this raises the level of the bed, making the lake shallower. Around the edges, where the depth is least, tall plants rooted in the sediment grow farther from the shore, raise the sediment further, and slowly advance toward the center. The lake is now "old," and its water is rich in nutrients. It is now said to be eutrophic (*eu* means "good").

While accumulating sediment makes the lake shallower, water is also lost from the lake by evaporation and transpiration. Water evaporates from the surface. Plants transport water through their roots, stems, and leaves, and it is released from pores, called stomata, in the leaves. This process is called transpiration.

Gradually, the lake becomes smaller as plants grow closer to its center and shallower as its bed rises and it loses water. It is now approaching the end of its life. Soon it is reduced to no more than a patch of wet ground. Then plants from the surrounding area establish themselves, and as they mature, the lake fades.

BOGS

Dying lakes do not always turn into dry land. Sometimes, especially in cool climates, they turn into bogs.

A RAISED BOG *(right)* **is a former lake or valley bog that has accumulated so much peat that its surface bulges upward.**

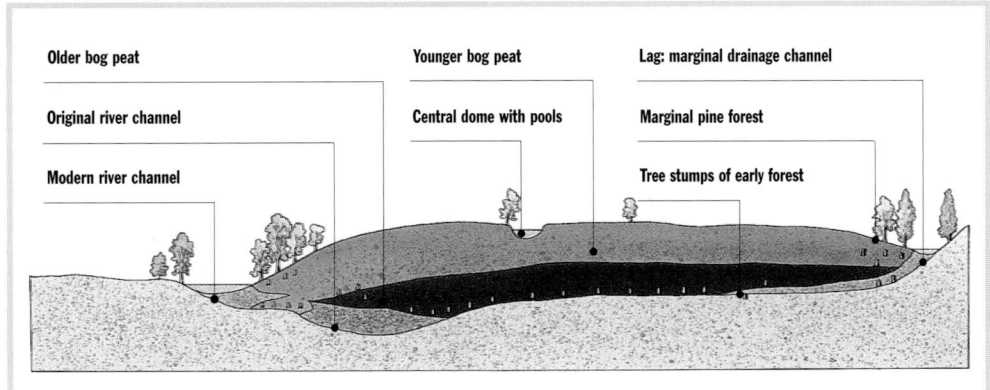

Older bog peat

Original river channel

Modern river channel

Younger bog peat

Central dome with pools

Lag: marginal drainage channel

Marginal pine forest

Tree stumps of early forest

Usually, the formation of a bog begins when the lake is colonized by a plant that grows across the surface as a floating mat, without being rooted in the mud at the bottom. The mat grows thicker, and other plants start growing on top of it. These are often rushes, or cotton grasses, but the most important flora is a species of moss belonging to the genus *Sphagnum*. Sphagnum mosses have cells that can absorb up to 20 times their own weight of water. They make the water beneath them very acid by absorbing calcium and releasing hydrogen; they also break down acids, releasing hydrogen.

Dead plant material sinks to the bottom, beneath the floating mass of vegetation, but in the acid, airless conditions the process of decomposition is slowed. The resulting mass of partially decomposed organic material is known as peat.

There are several types of bog. Valley bogs form in a hollow or valley bottom that is wet because of poor drainage. A former lake or valley bog may accumulate so much peat that its surface bulges upward. This is a raised bog. The surface of a bog may be well above the water table, and the plants growing on it may obtain all their water from the rain. The bog is then said to be ombrogenous (rain-fed). Ombrogenous bogs can form on almost level higher ground, where they are known as blanket bogs. These occur in the hills of northern Europe and North America.

Typical bogs dominated by mosses cover areas in the forest regions of Canada, northern Europe and Russia, and high rainfall areas of Britain. Tropical tree bogs (in which the peat is formed from tree remains) are found in Southeast Asia, South America, and Africa.

SWAMPS

In swamps the plant life is often dominated by trees, and there is no peat. Swamp water may be still or flowing, and it is stillwater swamps that are most likely to dry out. Various pines, palm trees, and broad-leaved trees are found in

BALD CYPRESS TREES
(Taxodium distichum)
grow in this swamp,
which is typical of
swamps covering large
parts of the Mississippi
delta in Louisiana in the
United States.

stillwater swamps. In North America one of the commonest species is the pond cypress (*Taxodium ascendens*). River swamps occur either beside a river or on the low ground behind the natural levee at the river bank.

The Everglades is a marsh-swamp region of 5,000 square miles (12,950 sq. km) in Florida in the United States. For much of the year it is a wide river, between 1 and 7 feet (0.3–2.0 m) deep, flowing south and carrying the overflow from Lake Okeechobee. It supports sawgrass (*Cladium jamaicense*) from 3 to 10 feet (1–3 m) tall with scattered woodlands.

Salt swamps are formed in regularly flooded areas of tropical and subtropical regions that are sheltered from strong wave action. In these

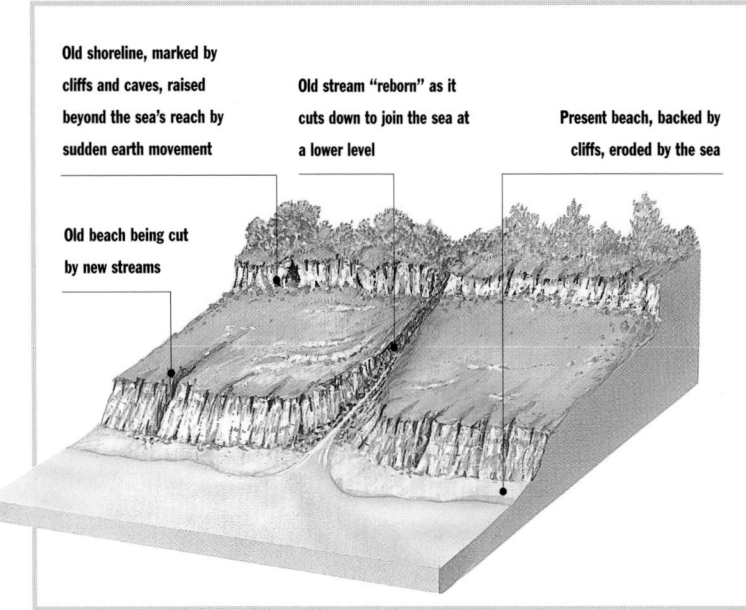

Old shoreline, marked by cliffs and caves, raised beyond the sea's reach by sudden earth movement

Old stream "reborn" as it cuts down to join the sea at a lower level

Present beach, backed by cliffs, eroded by the sea

Old beach being cut by new streams

ANCIENT COASTLINES can be recognized from raised beaches, formed when the sea level was higher or the land was lower. Sometimes a change in sea or land level leaves a section of the original coastline complete with cliffs and caves some distance inland.

conditions mangrove trees can form dense swamp forests. Mangroves grow only in salty conditions, and their roots project above the water surface, giving them access to the air (see page 39). There are about 90 species of mangroves. They grow best in mud, and their roots trap particles carried in the water flowing around them. This builds up the level of the surface on which they are growing, so the shoreline is gradually extended. At the same time the mangrove roots provide protected crevices, bowers, and surfaces that attract animals.

COASTS AND ESTUARIES

At estuaries the sea flows inland with each high tide, in many places twice a day. An estuary carries both fresh and salt water. These do not mix readily, because salt water is denser than

fresh water. As the tide rises, salt water moves upstream, but river water is still moving downstream. Depending on the shape of the estuary, the salt water may travel along the bottom as a wedge beneath the fresh water. In this type of estuary the surface water is fresh and flowing toward the sea, and beneath it there is salt water flowing inland. Alternatively, the fresh and salt water may form separate streams flowing parallel to each other but in opposite directions. It is more difficult to detect the two types of water when the tide is ebbing, because then they are both flowing in the same direction.

Flocculation

Rivers carry solid particles of various sizes. Where the river water meets salt water it is slowed; the river loses energy, and its ability to carry particles is reduced. The bigger of them—those the size of sand grains—sink to the bottom. This often happens at or just beyond the mouth of the river, and it produces a sandbar.

The very small particles are of silt, clay, and organic material. Many of them contain ions (atoms or molecules that have gained or lost electrons) that give them an electric charge. Seawater also contains ions—when dissolved in water, salt (NaCl) dissociates into sodium (Na^+) and chlorine (Cl^-) ions. Positive and negative ions join, and this has the effect of binding particles together into lumps—the process is called flocculation. The clumped particles sink to form mudbanks.

Coastline Changes

Coastlines are constantly changing, and some of the changes are on a large scale. During ice ages, for example, water is transferred from the sea to the ice sheets, and the sea level falls. When the ice melts, the sea level rises again. The land surface also rises and falls. Land beneath a thick ice sheet is depressed by the weight. When the ice melts, it rises to its former level.

Changing sea levels leave traces by which they can be recognized. What were once beaches with sand and seashells may be found high above the existing sea level and inland. These are called raised beaches. Many estuaries lie in valleys that used to be much farther inland and were then flooded by the rising sea. These

are called drowned valleys. The rising sea can change an entire area into a drowned landscape.

At the coast itself wave action cuts back hills, producing steep cliffs and headlands. In time headlands are also worn away, the most resistant rock surviving longest. Wave action is called destructive if it erodes the coast in this way. Waves can also be constructive. Eroded material is ground to small grains then deposited—usually on part of the same coast. There, it builds beaches. Sand blown inland by the wind forms dunes. Stretches of coastline also advance as spits that become dry land.

EROSION AND DEPOSITION. Cliffs, stacks, and headlands are produced by the erosive action of destructive waves. Beaches, sandbars, sand dunes, and spits are made from sand deposited by constructive waves. Material eroded from one section of coast is usually deposited elsewhere along the same coast.

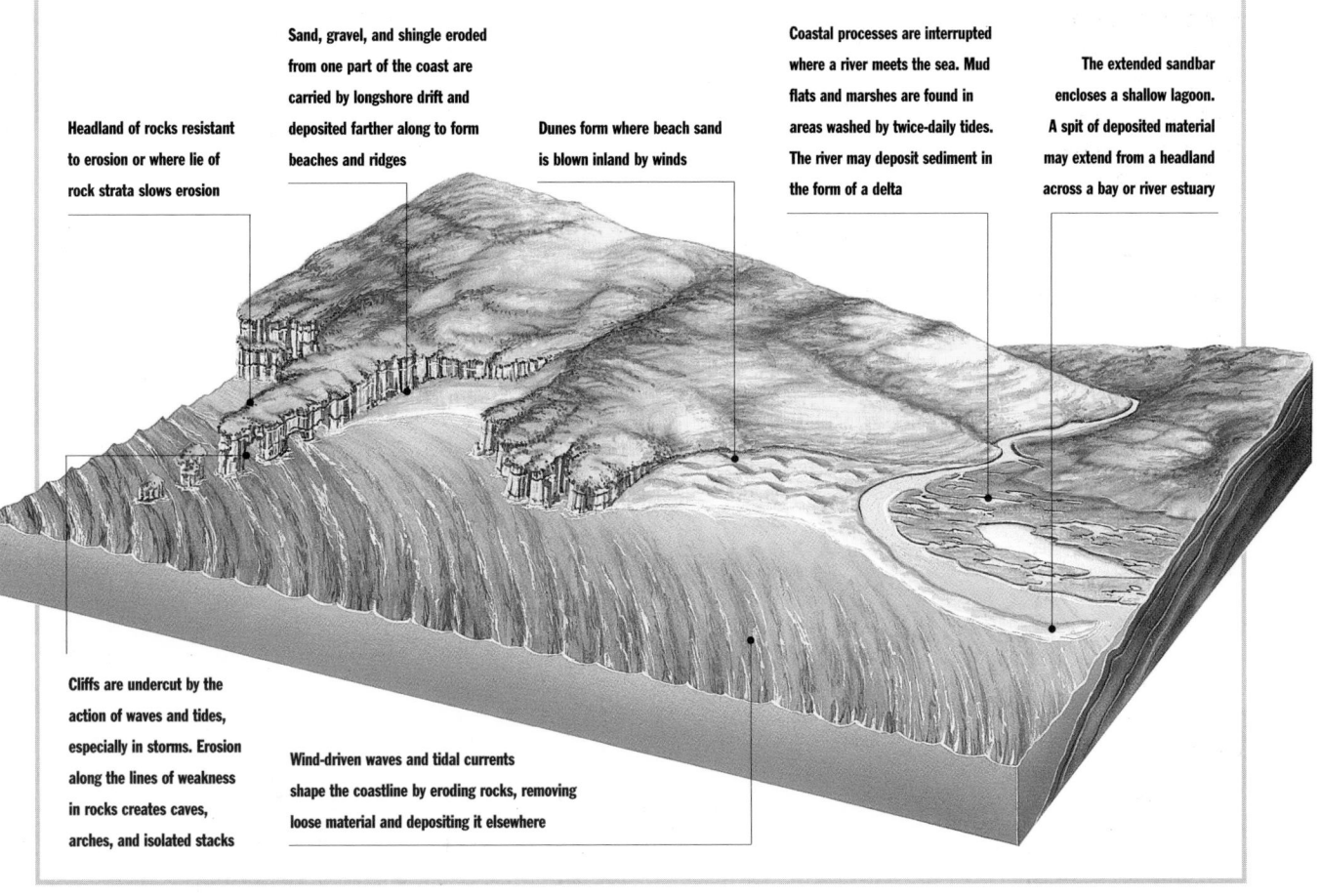

Sand, gravel, and shingle eroded from one part of the coast are carried by longshore drift and deposited farther along to form beaches and ridges

Coastal processes are interrupted where a river meets the sea. Mud flats and marshes are found in areas washed by twice-daily tides. The river may deposit sediment in the form of a delta

The extended sandbar encloses a shallow lagoon. A spit of deposited material may extend from a headland across a bay or river estuary

Headland of rocks resistant to erosion or where lie of rock strata slows erosion

Dunes form where beach sand is blown inland by winds

Cliffs are undercut by the action of waves and tides, especially in storms. Erosion along the lines of weakness in rocks creates caves, arches, and isolated stacks

Wind-driven waves and tidal currents shape the coastline by eroding rocks, removing loose material and depositing it elsewhere

The Natural World of Wetlands

*W*etlands are secret places. Often they are inaccessible, and many of their inhabitants dwell below the surface out of sight. Even where they can be examined it may require a very close, detailed study to reveal their richness. Yet they are rich, supporting a wide variety of plants and animals.

A RIVER ECOSYSTEM *(below)* in tropical South America. The relationships are the same as those found in rivers anywhere in the world.

Components of the ecosystem

1 Plant plankton (algae)
2 Amazonian water lily
3 Plant detritus
4 Animal plankton
5 Terecay turtle
6 Capybara
7 Neon tetra
8 Leporinus fish
9 Amazonian dolphin
10 Piranha fish
11 Giant arapaima
12 Cayman

All plants and animals die if they cannot obtain the oxygen they need for respiration. Aquatic animals—those that live in water—must take their oxygen from the water, but aquatic plants can take it from the air, as land plants do, provided their leaves float on or are held above the surface of the water.

Plants use the energy of sunlight in photosynthesis—the manufacture of sugars. In this process they use hydrogen from water (H_2O) and carbon (C) and oxygen (O_2) from carbon dioxide (CO_2), and they combine them into a simple sugar, glucose ($C_6H_{12}O_6$). Photosynthesis takes place in green leaves in the cells containing the light-sensitive pigment chlorophyll. The waste product is oxygen. Aquatic plants photosynthesize and release oxygen into the water around them, where it dissolves.

The water also contains some oxygen dissolved from the air. The greater the water surface exposed, the more oxygen can dissolve. White water, which splashes over and around stones in rivers, is well-oxygenated water.

Cold water can hold more dissolved oxygen than warm water. At 41°F (5°C), for example, water can hold about nine parts of oxygen to 1,000 parts of water. This is the per mill (‰) value. At 68°F (20°C) it can hold about 6.5‰. Raising the temperature of water decreases the amount of dissolved oxygen it contains. Heating also accelerates the rate at which organic matter is decomposed by bacteria. This is an oxidation process in which carbon (C) combines with oxygen (O_2) to form carbon dioxide (CO_2).

Aquatic animals depend on oxygen dissolved in the water around them. They extract

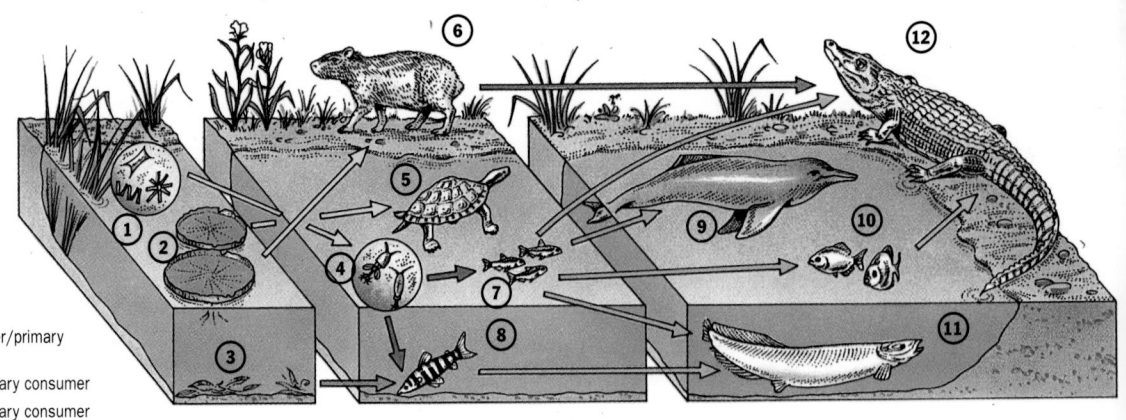

Energy flow

⇨ Primary producer/primary consumer
⇨ Primary/secondary consumer
⇨ Secondary/tertiary consumer
⇨ Dead material/consumer

Primary producers   **Herbivores**   **Carnivores**

FRESHWATER PLANTS AND ANIMALS need the oxygen that is dissolved in the water. The water in this river *(above)* is clear, fast-flowing, and well-oxygenated.

it by means of gills, organs that have very fine membranes and a very large surface area. The water is passed across the gills, and the oxygen crosses the membranes and enters the blood vessels. Species differ in the amount of dissolved oxygen they need, but all suffer if the water loses oxygen.. The most serious forms of freshwater pollution are those that reduce the concentration of dissolved oxygen.

AQUATIC ECOSYSTEMS

Rivers and lakes contain communities of bacteria, plants, and animals. Ecology is the scientific study of the relationships among all the members of these communities and between them and the physical and chemical conditions in which they live. If a community inhabits an

area that can be easily distinguished from the areas around it, the relationships within that community can be studied as an "ecological system," or "ecosystem" for short. A river or lake is quite different from the dry land adjacent to it, so it can be studied as an ecosystem.

Aquatic plants and plant material that falls into the water from the banks provide food for herbivorous animals. Because plants manufacture food from simple ingredients—water, carbon dioxide, and mineral compounds—they are called producers. In water some of the plants consist of a single cell, although the cells are sometimes joined together to make long filaments. The filaments are attached at one end to rocks and wave gently in the current like pennants (long flags) in the wind. Those that do not form filaments form a slimy coating on stones or other solid surfaces, or they drift freely in still or slow-moving water. Individuals are just visible as tiny green specks, but in large numbers they color the water green.

The animals that feed on the plants (herbivores) are primary consumers. Animals that feed on other animals (carnivores) are secondary consumers. Carnivores include beetles and the young of damselflies and dragonflies. These insects spend most of their lives as aquatic larvae (nymphs), and they are voracious predators. Some dragonfly nymphs will catch tadpoles and even small fish.

Predators can also be large. The northern pike (*Esox lucius*) and its close relative the muskellunge, or muskie (*E. masquinongy*), grow to a length of 5 feet (1.5 m) and feed mainly on other fish. One of the biggest, however, is the arapaima (*Arapaima gigas*), which lives in the Amazon and its tributaries. It grows to at least 10 feet (3 m) long. These are freshwater fish, and they could not survive in salt water.

FRESH WATER AND SALT

Most fish and aquatic invertebrates (animals without backbones) are able to live only in water of one kind or the other. Land mammals, including humans, cannot quench their thirst by drinking salt water.

Salmon and eels of the family Anguillidae are among the few species of fish that spend part of their lives at sea and part in fresh water.

Osmosis

Salt water is a weak solution of a wide variety of compounds, but principally of common salt (sodium chloride). In seawater the average salt concentration is 35‰.

Many biological membranes, including cell walls, are partially permeable. This means that some molecules are able to pass through them, but not others. Some partially permeable membranes are semipermeable. These allow water molecules to pass, but not molecules of substances dissolved in the water. This selective permeability allows nutrients to enter cells and waste products to leave.

Separate two aqueous solutions of different strengths by a semipermeable membrane, however, and water molecules will pass through

THE ARAPAIMA (*Arapaima gigas*) is a freshwater fish that grows to at least 10 feet (3 m) long and lives in rivers of tropical South America. It has a "swim bladder" (air bladder)— an air-filled sac that is connected to its throat and acts as a kind of lung, allowing it to enter waters containing little dissolved oxygen and to regulate its buoyancy at different depths.

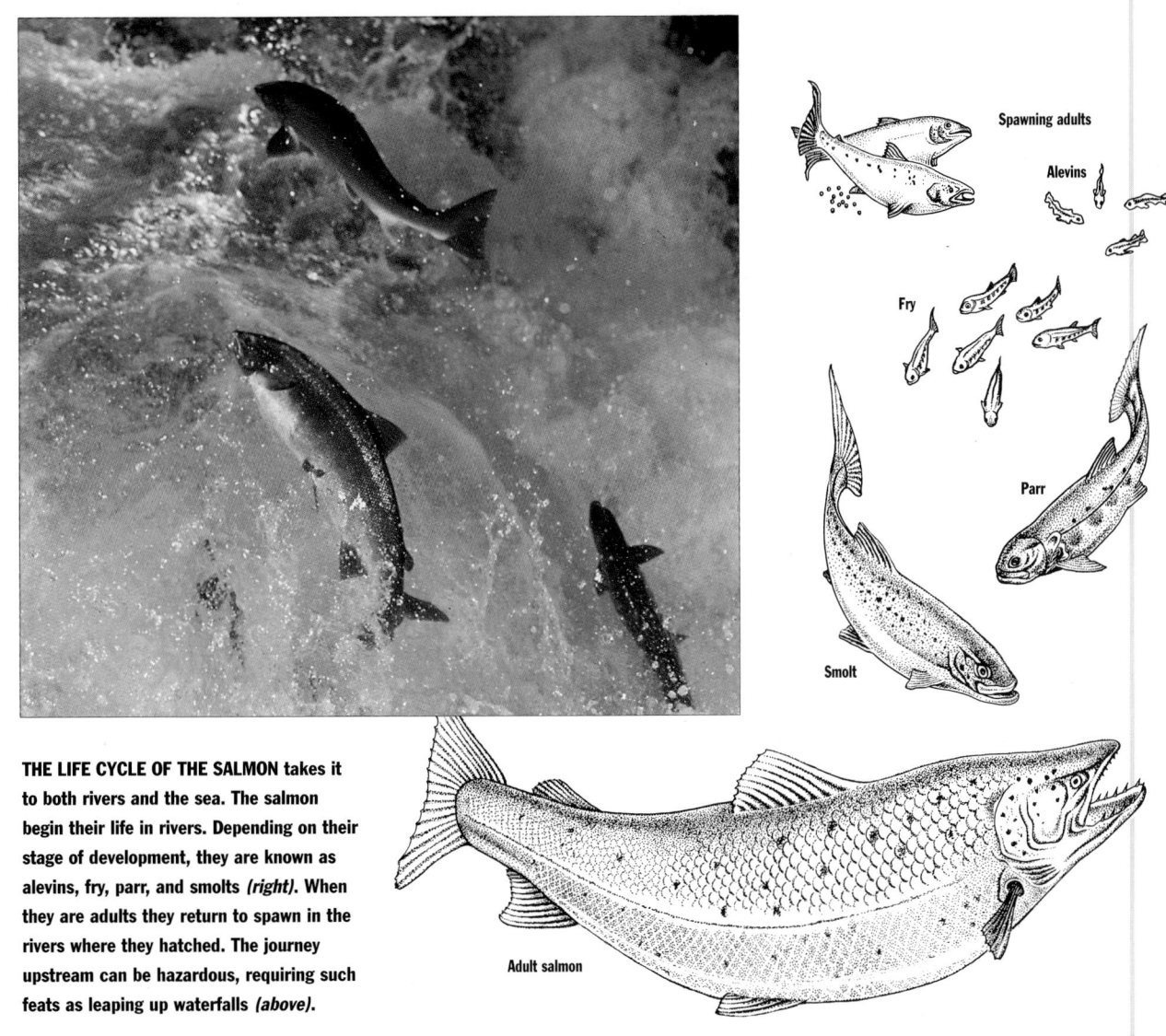

THE LIFE CYCLE OF THE SALMON takes it to both rivers and the sea. The salmon begin their life in rivers. Depending on their stage of development, they are known as alevins, fry, parr, and smolts *(right)*. When they are adults they return to spawn in the rivers where they hatched. The journey upstream can be hazardous, requiring such feats as leaping up waterfalls *(above)*.

Spawning adults

Alevins

Fry

Parr

Smolt

Adult salmon

the membrane from the weaker to the stronger solution. This movement will continue until the two solutions are of equal concentration. The process is called osmosis.

In freshwater animals—and land animals that drink fresh water—the body fluids and cell contents are weak saline solutions. If much saltier water comes into contact with cell walls, water will leak through the walls. This will dehydrate the cells and therefore the body

tissues. If the animal is unable to obtain or return to fresh water, it will die.

Osmosis affects marine organisms in the opposite way. The salinity of their body fluids and cell contents is about the same as that of seawater. Expose them to fresh water, and water will leak across their membranes from the weaker to the stronger solution. The water will flood into their tissues and cells until their walls rupture.

Migrating Salmon

Many species of salmon (family Salmonidae) begin their lives in rivers and then return to the sea. Fish that migrate from the sea up rivers to breed are said to be anadromous. (Those that migrate down rivers to the sea in order to breed are catadromous—they include some eels).

Adult salmon spawn (lay and fertilize eggs) in rivers. The eggs hatch as alevins; for about six weeks they are nourished from the yolk sacs attached to them. Then the fry (young fish) start feeding. When they develop blue-gray "finger-marks" along their sides, they are called parr.

When the fish are 4–8 inches (10–20 cm) long (between one and five years), they turn silver. At this stage they are ready to migrate to the sea and they are known as smolts. They enter the sea and remain there for up to four years. Then they return to spawn in the rivers where they were born, sometimes leaping up waterfalls in the journey upstream.

From the time they enter the river until they have spawned, the adults do not feed. After spawning they are called kelts. Many die on their way back to the sea.

FRESHWATER BIRDS

Many small animals live in rivers and lakes, and several species of birds and mammals take advantage of this rich source of food.

Dippers (water ouzels)—birds of the family Cinclidae—are possibly the most remarkable of all freshwater birds. They are small, plump birds, about 7 inches (18 cm) long. All five species are very similar. They are strong fliers, often to be seen skimming fast and low over the water.

They are found throughout much of Europe and Asia and on the western side of North and Central America, and northern South America. The most widespread American species is the

THE DIPPER swims well underwater and can walk along the riverbed in search of prey. This is the European dipper *(Cinclus cinclus)*.

American dipper (*Cinclus mexicanus*) and the commonest Old World species is *C. cinclus*, the dipper or white-breasted dipper.

The name "dipper" refers to the habit all dippers share of bobbing up and down while perched on a rock in the middle of a river. What is remarkable about them is that they are able to walk into the water from the bank and then continue along the bed of a river, beneath the water, as they hunt for the invertebrate animals and small fish on which they feed. They also swim under the water and can remain submerged for up to 30 seconds. Their bodies are well insulated against the cold, and they can forage for food beneath the ice.

Kingfishers

Kingfishers are spectacular. The Eurasian kingfisher (*Alcedo atthis*) is tiny, about 6.5 inches (16.5 cm) long, with a chestnut-colored underside, but a back and wings of a brilliant, iridescent blue-green. It appears as a flash of bright blue darting this way and that over the water and is unmistakable. It feeds mainly on fish, which it catches by diving into the water at an angle of about 45°. It closes its eyes while it is catching its prey; they are still closed when it emerges from the water. The bird then carries its fish to a convenient perch, beats it against the perch a few times, then swallows it head-first. Kingfishers also eat some invertebrate animals. Insects—some caught in flight—make up about 20 percent of the diet of Eurasian kingfishers.

The belted kingfisher (*Megaceryle alcyon*) of North America hunts in the same way as its Eurasian relative. It is a blue-gray bird, about 10 inches (25 cm) long, with a prominent crest.

A pair of belted kingfishers occupies a home territory along the bank of a pond or stream and will defend it vigorously against intruders. Both species nest in a hole they dig in the bank.

FRESHWATER MAMMALS

Otters are among the best-known freshwater mammals. They are members of the family Mustelidae, which includes weasels, ferrets,

THE EURASIAN KINGFISHER has brilliant, iridescent, blue-green back and wings and a chestnut body. It is usually seen darting across the water like a flash of blue light. Like other kingfishers, it nests in a burrow that it digs in the banks along rivers.

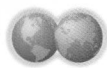

minks, badgers, and skunks. Otters are highly intelligent predators.

Both otters and minks have taken to life in and beside the water. Otters are truly amphibious, being entirely at home in the water and, except for the almost wholly aquatic sea otter, no less at home on dry land. Minks live beside water and swim well, but are less committed to an aquatic life than otters—although they have partially webbed feet.

There are 12 species of otters in six genera, but most widespread and best known are the six species of the genus *Lutra*. Four are American, one Eurasian, and one lives in Sumatra. Otters eat whatever they find easiest to catch. They will eat frogs, ducks, and other water birds, as well as fish, and are more likely to take slow-moving fish such as eels and sticklebacks than fast swimmers such as trout and salmon. They need to feed several times a day because their very active behavior and the cold water in which they spend so much of their time require a large amount of "fuel."

Mink look very similar to otters, but are smaller. The mink has a round head and slightly bushy tail, the otter has a flat head and a long, smooth tail that is very thick at the base. American, or eastern, mink (*Mustela vision*) and the European mink (*M. lutreola*) are much more versatile than otters. They will dive for fish and aquatic invertebrates, but they also catch young rabbits, voles and other rodents, and water birds. In North America and parts of Russia muskrats (*Ondatra zibethicus*) are an important part of their diet.

American mink from Canada were brought to Britain in 1929 for farming. Soon after that

there were reports of mink living wild, and they have been breeding in Britain since the 1950s. European mink, which are smaller, do not occur in Britain.

Beavers

Beavers are herbivorous, squirrel-like rodents. There are two species, the North American and European beavers (*Castor canadensis* and *C. fiber* respectively).

BEAVERS *(left)* are the largest rodents in North America and Europe. They live in ponds, lakes, rivers, and streams. Beavers live in family units; the parents have a long-term relationship and care for their young—"kits"—for two years before they reach adulthood. The kits are able to swim within a few hours of birth, but they spend weeks practicing the complex home-building process.

THE BEAVER LODGE AND DAM *(below)* are built on a base of stones using branches and sticks. These are sealed with sods of earth and aquatic plants. The lodge has a single living chamber above the water and is reached by burrows with entrances on the lake bed. The adults and yearlings build the dams, and females are more active in the process than males.

In spring and summer beavers will eat grass and herbs, but in later summer and fall they prefer the tender bark from the topmost branches of trees, especially willow, birch, aspen, and poplar. In the fall they gather small branches and store them underwater as food for the winter.

Like other rodents, they have large incisor teeth that grow constantly and are worn down by gnawing. They also have a remarkable ability to cut down trees for food and building materials. A pair of adult beavers can gnaw through a tree 4 inches (10 cm) thick in about 15 minutes. They have no control over the direction the tree falls. Beavers are sometimes killed when the trees fall on them.

Beavers are social animals, and live in family groups, usually of a pair of adults and their offspring from one or more years, so the home accommodates about ten animals.

The beaver burrow is known as a lodge. Beavers also build "dams" across streams to create an area safe from predators.

The lodge and dam are made from stones overlaid with sticks and sealed with water weeds and sods of earth. Most dams are about 5 feet (1.5 m) long, but they can be very much longer—and up to 12 feet (3.7 m) high. Water behind the dam forms a pool, usually about 3 feet (1 m) deep.

The same technique is used to build the lodge. It has one living chamber, clear of the water, to which access is gained through tunnels with entrances on the bottom of the lake. Above water, mud is plastered onto the sticks to seal them, except above the center of the living

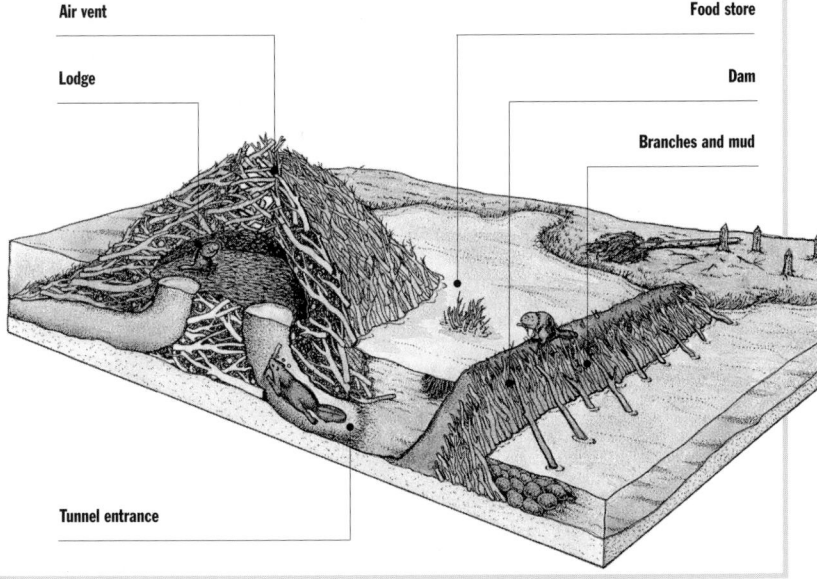

Air vent

Lodge

Tunnel entrance

Food store

Dam

Branches and mud

The animal's flat, scaly tail, heavy torpedo-shaped body, and short legs with webbed feet are well suited to movement in the water. Its tail acts as a rudder and provides propulsion when pulsated in the water. Beavers also use their tails to make a slapping movement on the water to warn others of imminent danger. When they dive, they close their throat, ears, and nostrils, and their eyes are protected with a thin transparent membrane.

A SHALLOW LAKE
(opposite) **in a coniferous forest in northern Finland. The reeds growing at its edges are advancing into the water. Small willows are also growing at the water's edge.**

AN ECOSYSTEM IN A FRESHWATER LAKE
(below), **in this case Lake Baikal in Russia, the largest freshwater lake in Eurasia and the deepest in the world. It is the home of the Baikal seal** *(Phoca sibirica)*.

Components of the ecosystem

1   Plant plankton
2   Animal plankton
3   Herbivorous protist
4   Freshwater shrimp
5   Freshwater shrimp
6   Osprey
7   Baikal seal
8   Pike
9   Carp
10 Transparent bottom-dwelling fish

Energy flow

⇨ Primary producer/primary consumer
⇨ Primary/secondary consumer
⇨ Secondary/tertiary consumer
⇨ Dead material/consumer

chamber, where the sticks remain unsealed for ventilation. In winter the outside of the lodge often freezes, making it very strong indeed.

The occupants spend the winter inside the lodge, where it is a little warmer than it is outside. For the rest of the year building and maintaining the lodge and dam take up a good deal of their time.

The beavers' home is not permanent, however. The dam traps soil particles and other material carried by the water. Little by little this accumulates as a layer of sediment, raising the bed of the pond or lake and making it shallower. After several generations of beavers have lived there, the lodge becomes uninhabitable and the family moves elsewhere, leaving the pond or lake to fill with sediment. It can then become a very fertile meadow.

LAKE ECOSYSTEMS

Lakes form wherever there is a depression in the land surface with a base of impermeable rock and a source of water to maintain the level—circumstances that can occur in a wide variety of conditions.

Not all lakes contain fresh water. Great Salt Lake in Utah in the United States is a shallow lake containing sodium chloride and other mineral salts washed into it. It loses water mainly by evaporation, so its salinity is high and variable; it averages 23‰. This is less salty than the ocean, which is an average 35‰. Neither is nearly as salty as the Dead Sea, between Israel and Jordan, in which the salinity is about 270‰. (Despite its name, the Dead Sea is a lake. It has no link with the ocean, and it is smaller than Great Salt Lake.)

Salt lakes support only single-celled organisms that thrive in the extreme conditions, but mature freshwater lakes are densely populated. The primary producers are green plants, as they are in most ecosystems. These include phytoplankton—single-celled algae that float near the surface. The plants can grow because of the bacteria that live in the water or in the bottom of the lake on the mud. The bacteria break down complex organic molecules, releasing simpler molecules, which the plants can absorb as nutrients.

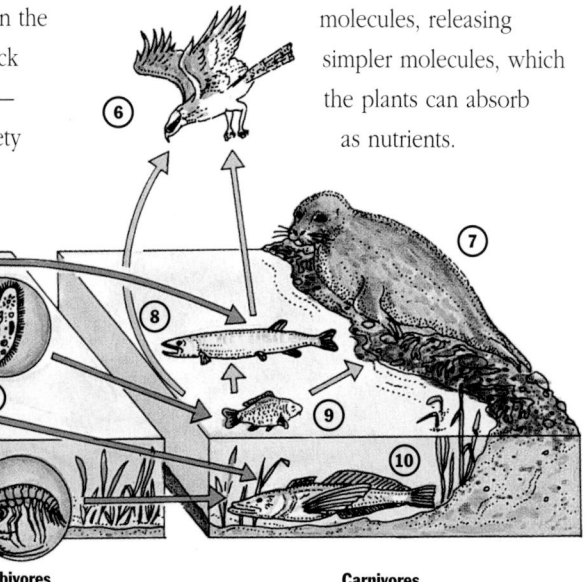

Primary producers   **Herbivores**   **Carnivores**

Tiny animals—zooplankton—feed on the phytoplankton, and when they die these organisms, together comprising the plankton, sink to the bottom and are consumed by the community living in the sediment. This includes worms, snails, and the larvae of some insects such as midges.

Some fish feed on the bottom of lakes. Carp (*Cyprinus carpio*), catfish, bullheads, and many other species have mouths adapted for sucking. Catfishes and bullheads belong to the order Siluriformes (bullheads are *Ictalurus* species; there are several genera of catfishes). They strain organic particles from the mud. Other fish—and the young of most fish—feed on the plankton. Some fish are carnivores, feeding on smaller fish.

Plants growing in shallow water near the lake edge provide food and nesting sites for water birds. Other birds hunt for fish and small animals, usually by diving for them.

Water bugs and water beetles are common in lakes in temperate climates. The adult insects do not possess gills, so they cannot breathe in water. However, water beetles and water bugs manage to hunt beneath the water surface. They capture a bubble of

air and take it down with them, returning to the surface when it is exhausted.

Water beetles belonging to the family Dytiscidae are fiercely predatory. (Aquarium owners are advised to avoid them because they will attack even medium-sized fish, including goldfish.) Frogs and newts are part of their regular diet. Backswimmers (family Notonectidae) are no less fierce. Whirligig beetles (family Gyrinidae), which are also carnivorous, live on the surface and use their legs as paddles.

Small insects are so abundant in temperate lakes that one plant has adapted to "eating" them. The bladderwort (*Utricularia vulgaris*) has no roots. It has long, leafy stems that float on and below the surface. Some of the leaves bear tiny bladders, or air-filled sacs. Minute freshwater crustaceans (such as water fleas) touching sensory hairs on the bladder cause it to spring open. This sucks the prey into the bladder, where it is digested. Bladderworts are also found in bogs (see page 33).

Lakeside Birds and Mammals

Tall reeds and rushes growing in the shallow water at the edge of lakes provide shelter for several species of birds. Grebes (family Podicipedidae) nest in this type of vegetation, as does the bittern (*Botaurus stellaris*), a European member of the heron family (Ardeidae). The bittern responds to disturbance by standing rigidly upright with its bill pointing upward so it becomes almost invisible against the pattern of vertical plant stems.

The muskrat (*Ondatra zibethicus*) is a North American amphibious rodent that resembles a

THE BLADDERWORT has no roots, but many leafy stems that float on and below the surface. There are small bladders on some of the leaves. When a bladder opens, it inflates, drawing in water and any tiny animal in the water. The mouth of the bladder then closes, and the prey is digested.

Sensitive trigger hairs open trap door

Minute animal activates trigger hair

Flowers open above water

Leaf

Bladder

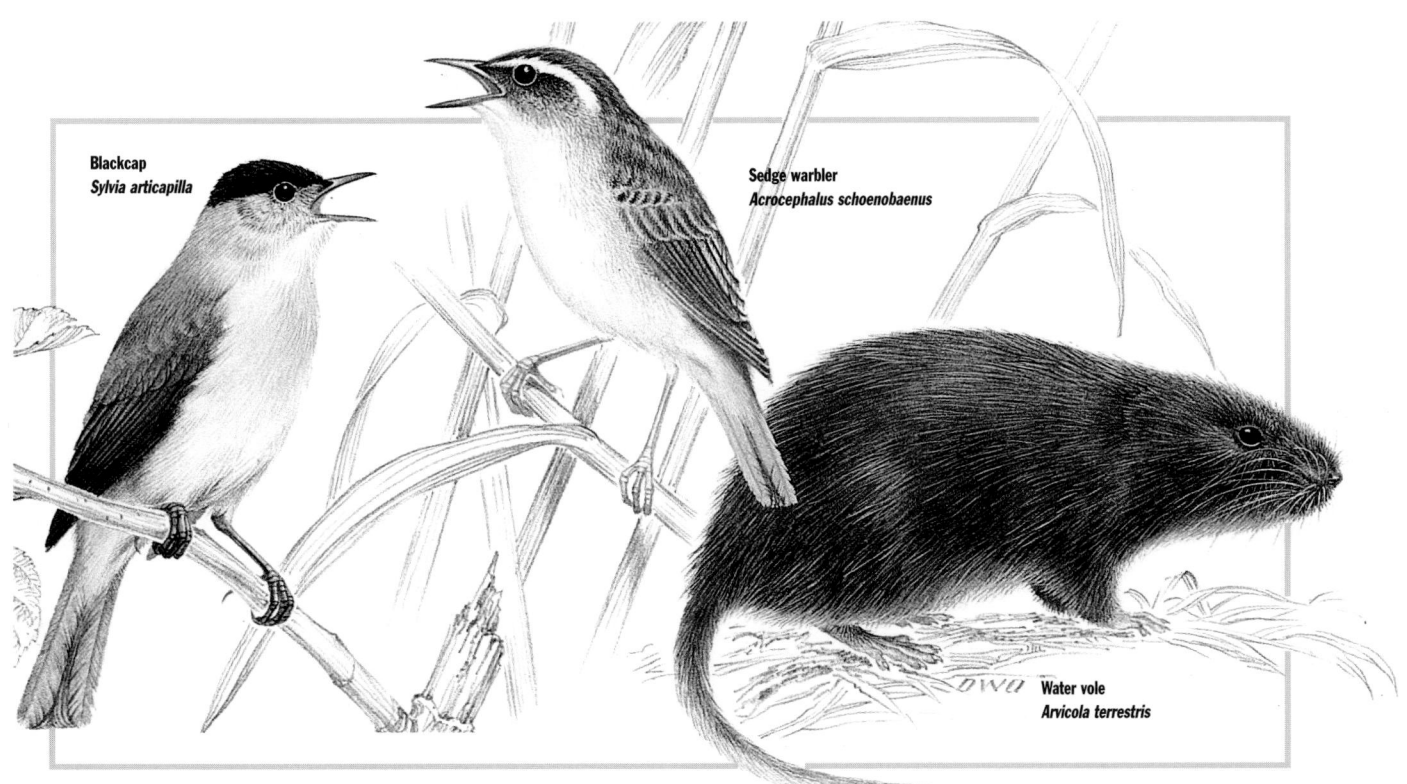

Blackcap
Sylvia articapilla

Sedge warbler
Acrocephalus schoenobaenus

Water vole
Arvicola terrestris

beaver. It is about 12 inches (30 cm) long with a tail about 9.5 inches (24 cm) long and spends much of its time in the water. Its hind feet are webbed, and its tail is naked and flattened vertically, allowing it to be used as a rudder.

Muskrats, like beavers, build lodges sometimes in shallow water at the edge of a lake. A muskrat lodge is made from sticks, leaves, grass, and reeds, and inside it there is a sleeping platform well clear of the water. The lodge may accommodate up to ten muskrats. More often, though, the muskrats live in a burrow excavated in the bank.

The European equivalent of a muskrat is the water vole (*Arvicola terrestris*), which can be found around lakes and rivers. The animal was immortalized as "Ratty" in the popular children's story *The Wind in the Willows*. The water vole is about half the size of the muskrat—about 6.5

inches (16.5 cm) long with a 3-inch (7.5-cm) tail.

The water vole dives and swims well, although its feet are not webbed. It is easily mistaken for a rat (rats also swim well), and it is sometimes called a water rat.

Water voles sometimes nest on the surface among dense vegetation, but most commonly they live in a burrow in the bank of a river or lake.

AMPHIBIANS

Amphibians are vertebrates (animals with backbones) that typically live on land but breed in the water (the word is from the Greek for "double life"). They rarely drink water and need to keep their skins moist.

BIRDS AND MAMMALS OF THE LAKESIDE. The blackcap and sedge warbler are small, insectivorous birds found throughout Europe. The sedge warbler nests in reed beds and other dense vegetation near water. The blackcap is a woodland bird that may visit lakes to feed. The water vole, also called the water rat, is a small amphibious mammal that lives beside lakes and rivers.

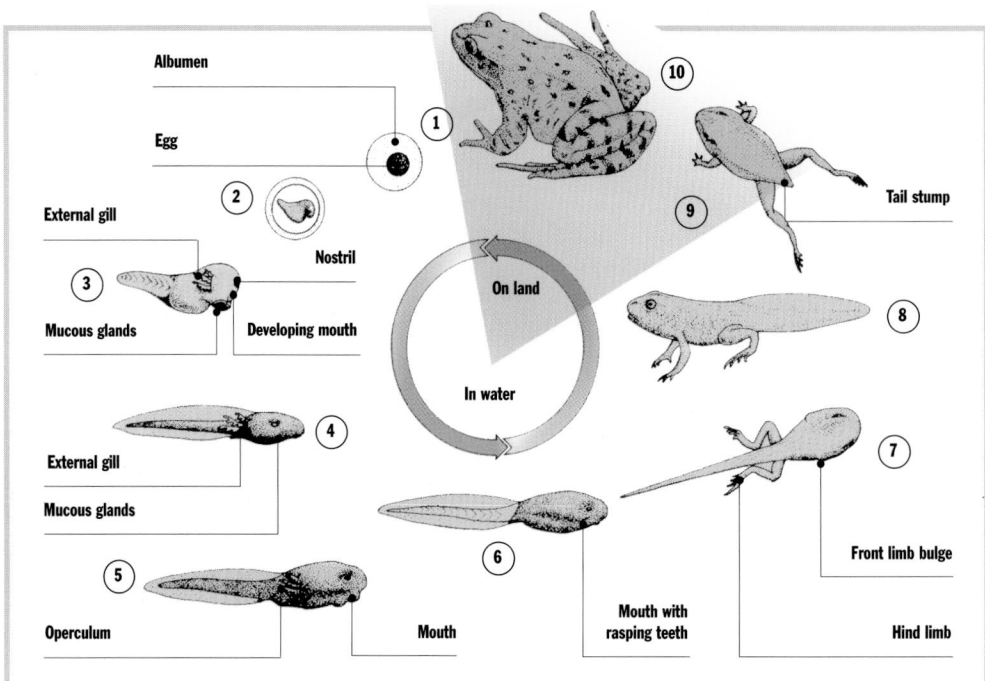

THE LIFE CYCLE OF THE FROG showing its development from egg to tadpole to adult.

1 **Egg**

2 **Embryo ready to hatch about five days after fertilization**

3 **One day after hatching: the tadpole absorbs oxygen through its skin, attaches to weeds by mucous glands, and feeds on the remainder of yolk in intestine**

4 **Two to three days after hatching: the mouth opens, the external gills become functional; the tadpole starts to feed on microscopic plants rasped from pond weeds**

5 **Six days after hatching: external gills start to shrivel and the operculum grows over the gills**

6 **Three weeks after hatching: the external gills have gone; the tadpole breathes with internal gills and grows considerably**

7 **Eight to ten weeks after hatching: the tadpole's hind limbs are well formed with front limbs bulging below operculum to emerge later from the spiracle; the lungs have formed internally and the tadpole gulps air from the surface; the tadpole changes to carnivorous diet**

8 **Twelve weeks after hatching: front legs appear, the tail starts to shorten; the eyes become more prominent, and the mouth broadens**

9 **About 16 weeks after hatching: the frog is ready for land; its tail is reabsorbed**

10 **The adult frog is ready to breed in four years**

The evolution of vertebrate animals began in water. Fishes were the first vertebrates to appear and to emerge from water. Amphibians, which evolved from the Rhipidistia, a group of fishes that is now extinct, took this development much further. They are able to spend much longer out of water, and most amphibians have legs. In time reptiles took the next step in the colonization of dry land by vertebrates.

Amphibians first appeared more than 360 million years ago. They comprise a class, Amphibia, and although they are less abundant today than they were until about 250 million years ago, there are still about 3,000 species. Those alive today fall into three groups. Caecilians (order Apoda) burrow in the ground and look like big earthworms. They are found only in the tropics and subtropics. More familiar are frogs and toads (order Anura) and salamanders and newts (order Urodela). There is no scientific difference between newts and salamanders, or between frogs and toads.

Amphibians' eggs are contained in an envelope of gelatinous material (albumen), but they lack an amnion, the membrane that encloses the developing embryo of a reptile, bird, or mammal, and they have no shells. This means the eggs must remain in a moist environment to avoid drying out. A few species produce live young, so the necessary moist environment is provided inside the body of the mother, but most amphibians lay their eggs in water. The young (larvae) breathe with gills.

Adults of most species have lungs and breathe air by closing the nostrils and raising the floor of the mouth to force air into the lungs—this is called buccal respiration. They also breathe by absorbing oxygen through their skins and into blood vessels—this is called cutaneous respiration. Amphibian skin contains glands that secrete mucus to keep it moist and allow gases to be exchanged through it.

The Life Cycle of the Frog

The European common frog (*Rana temporaria*) lays its eggs in still, shallow water, and they are fertilized externally. Masses of eggs, called spawn, hatch after about five days. At first the tadpole lives attached to a plant and feeds on the remains of its yolk, absorbing oxygen through its skin. A few days later its external gills become functional. The tadpole becomes mobile and starts feeding on plant material. Then the external gills shrink, the operculum (a hard, bony flap) grows over the gill chamber, and the tadpole starts breathing with its internal gills.

Over the following weeks the tadpole grows rapidly. By the time its hind legs have formed, the tadpole has also developed lungs and starts taking gulps of air at the surface of the water. At this stage its diet becomes carnivorous. The front legs appear, the tail starts to shrink, and the head becomes more froglike—the mouth widens and the eyes grow more prominent. The frog leaves the water when it is about 16 weeks old.

Newts and Salamanders

All newts are fully amphibious. Their larvae have external gills and look much like tadpoles. Adult newts have lungs, but they also absorb oxygen through their skins and mouth linings.

NEWTS AND SALAMANDERS. Like other amphibians, they absorb water through their skins and need a moist habitat in which to live. The larval stage can last for a few days or years; at this stage the animals have external gills. They feed on small animals such as insects, worms, and snails.

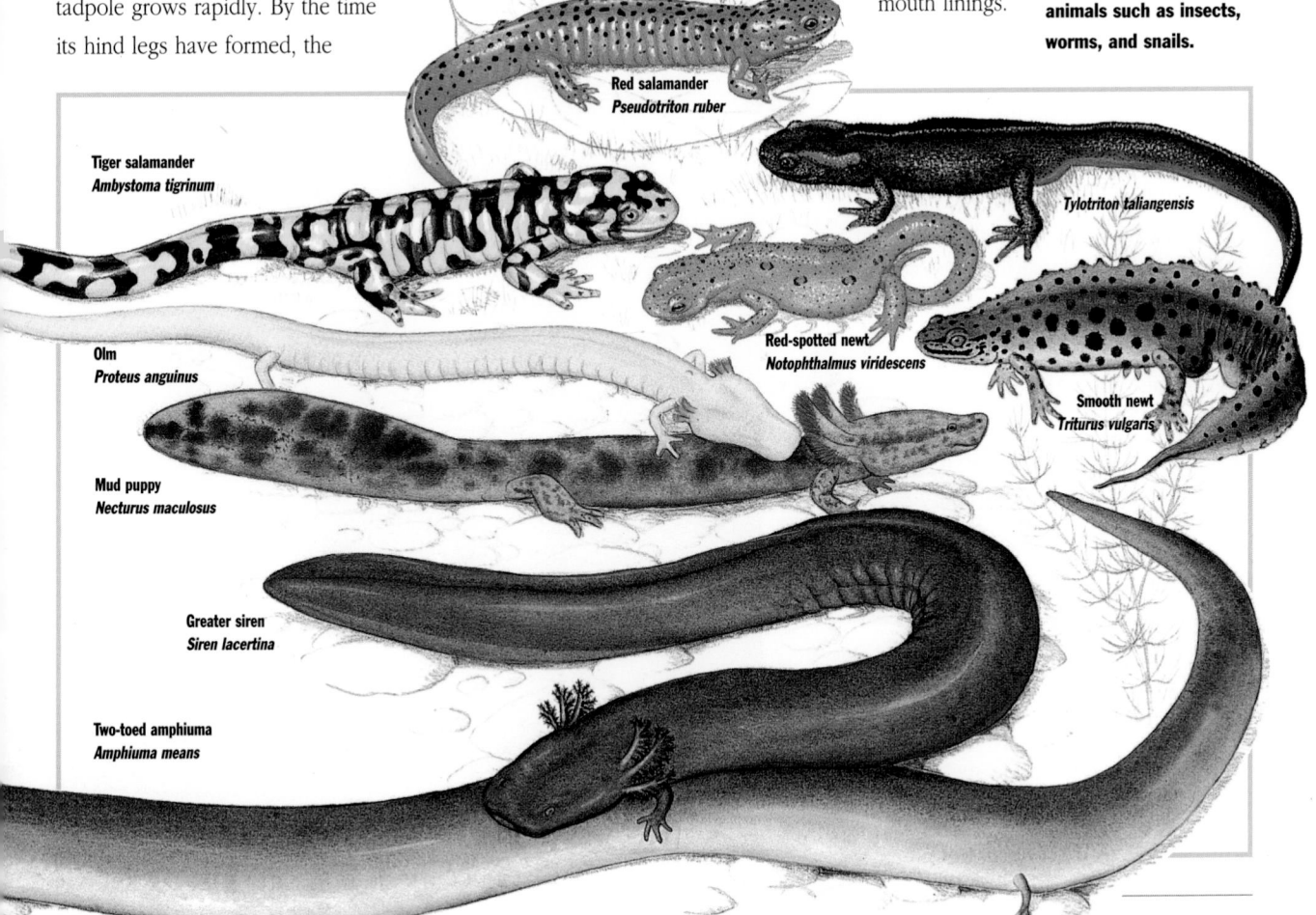

Red salamander
Pseudotriton ruber

Tiger salamander
Ambystoma tigrinum

Tylotriton taliangensis

Olm
Proteus anguinus

Red-spotted newt
Notophthalmus viridescens

Smooth newt
Triturus vulgaris

Mud puppy
Necturus maculosus

Greater siren
Siren lacertina

Two-toed amphiuma
Amphiuma means

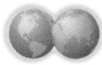
Salamanders are more variable. Some species are amphibious, but others are entirely terrestrial or entirely aquatic. The aquatic species, such as the olm (*Proteus anguinus*), greater siren (*Siren lacertina*), and mud puppy (*Necturus maculosus*), retain their external gills throughout their lives. Some have lost their lungs.

All members of the Plethodontidae, the family with the largest number of species and the greatest geographical range of any salamanders, lack lungs. They live in fast-flowing, well-oxygenated streams, where they can absorb oxygen through their skin and mouth lining. The absence of lungs makes them less buoyant, so they walk on the bottom in search of food.

Salamanders are just as flexible in the ways they develop. Paedogenesis is common. This is reproduction by animals that in every other respect are still larvae. The axolotl (*Ambystoma mexicanum*) is the most famous example, but there are many more, especially among cave-dwelling salamanders, such as the European olm.

The red-spotted newt (*Notophthalmus viridescens*), of eastern North America, starts life as an aquatic larva. After several months it may turn bright orange and move onto land. It is then called a red eft—and its skin secretions are highly poisonous. The eft lives three to seven years on land, then undergoes a second change into an aquatic adult.

Not all members of the species go through this sequence. Most of those in lowland habitats change directly from larva into an adult or into an adult that retains gills. Those living in the mountains are most likely to spend time as efts; this gives them time to find new aquatic habitats in which their descendants can live.

Components of the ecosystem

1 Cotton grass
2a and b Sundew
3 Sphagnum moss
4 Plant detritus
  5 Peat
    6 Herbivorous insects
    7 Linnet
    8 Worms, larvae, mollusks
    9 Willow tit
    10 Hen harrier
    11 Gray wagtail
    12 Common frog
13 Snipe

Primary producers **Herbivores** **Carnivores**

Energy flow

→ Primary producer/ primary consumer
→ Primary/secondary consumer
→ Secondary/tertiary consumer
→ Dead material/ consumer or decomposed
→ Death

LIFE IN BOGS

Bog moss (various *Sphagnum* species) is the key to the formation and survival of the bog community. The moss absorbs minerals from the water and makes it more acid. It also absorbs water (including rain) and holds it like a sponge. This helps maintain moist conditions.

Bog plants form a mat floating on water and isolated from the groundwater containing plant nutrients. Cold temperatures, the lack of oxygen and minerals, and the acidity of the water make it difficult for the bacteria and fungi that would ordinarily decompose organic material and release nitrogen in a form plant roots can absorb. Consequently, members of the bog mat community live in an environment that is very poor in plant nutrients. Insect-"eating" has evolved in some plant groups as a means of boosting their nutrient supply.

Bog violet (*Pinguicula vulgaris*) is called butterwort because it is said to make milk coagulate. It is a carnivorous plant that traps insects by curling over its leaf margins, then digests them with enzymes it secretes.

The sundew (about 80 *Drosera* species) is also an insect-eater. It has oval leaves covered with sticky "hairs" that close and trap small insects landing on them.

In the pitcher plants (*Sarracenia* species) of eastern North America the leaves are modified into the shape of pitchers, called sarcophagi, in which they trap insects. The commonest species, *S. purpurea*, is known as huntsman's horn or huntsman's cup and is an ornamental (a plant cultivated for show or decoration).

Another carnivorous plant, bladderwort, which lives in lakes and ponds (see page 28), is also found in bogs.

Invertebrates and Insects

Small pools of water collect in the sarcophagi of pitcher plants. A variety of single-celled organisms and tiny invertebrates live in these pools. The environment is well suited to species of insects that spend much of their lives as aquatic larvae. Various midges (mosquito-like insects of the family Chironomidae) and one species of mosquito (*Wyeomeia smithii*) spend their larval stages in the pitcher plants and avoid being consumed by them.

A BOG ECOSYSTEM provides only limited amounts of plant nutrients. Insectivorous plants obtain some of their nutrients by capturing and digesting insects, which are abundant.

BOGBEAN OR BUCKBEAN (*Menyanthes trifoliata*) (opposite) grows in bogs and spreads by means of its creeping stems. It occurs throughout high latitudes in the Northern Hemisphere.

Some of the insects common in bogs are fierce predators. Dragonflies eat other insects and tadpoles during their long larval stage. When they become flying adults, they continue to hunt, catching butterflies and mosquitos. They are themselves hunted by birds.

Bogs also provide ideal habitats for invertebrate animals such as worms (including leeches) and snails.

ESTUARIES AND SALT MARSHES

As the tide rises, it brings sand and nutrients and spreads them over the area it covers in an estuary. This enriches the estuary but also makes it a difficult place for plants and animals to live because the salinity varies so much. At high tide conditions are very saline. At low tide fresh water flows past and through the soft mud and sand and covers a large area. Periods of heavy rain also increase the amount of fresh water reaching the estuary.

Plants that can tolerate the high salinity are called halophytes. They include the plants known variously as saltwort, glasswort, samphire, and marsh samphire (*Salicornia* species)—and in Europe and Asia the sea aster (*Aster tripolium*). These plants cope with the variable salinity by storing water in their tissues—they are succulents. Other halophytes maintain the concentration of salts in their sap at a high enough level to allow some water to enter from the salt water in which they grow.

There is another problem to be overcome. Although the surface of the wetland in an estuary is exposed at low tide, below the surface conditions are permanently waterlogged. Every space between the solid particles is filled with water, and air is excluded. Plant roots must have access to air, and some, including cord grasses (*Spartina* species), achieve this by means of special tissue, called aerenchyma, that has large spaces between the cells. These are filled with air brought down to them from the part of the plant that stands above the surface. At low tide, when parts of the root are exposed, gases are exchanged between the roots and the atmosphere.

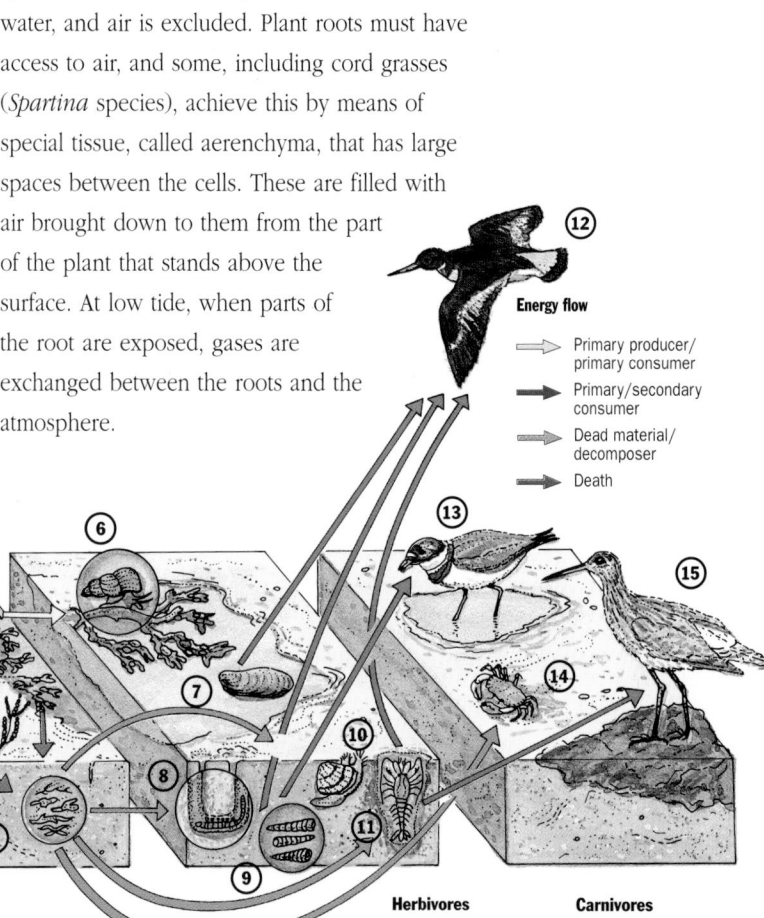

Components of the ecosystem

1 Sea aster
2 Glasswort
3 Townsend's cord grass
4 Bladderwrack
5 Detritus
6 Periwinkle
7 Mussel
8 Lugworm
9 Spire shells
10 Cockle
11 Shrimp
12 Oystercatcher
13 Ringed plover
14 Crab
15 Redshank

Energy flow

⟹ Primary producer/ primary consumer
➡ Primary/secondary consumer
⟹ Dead material/ decomposer
➡ Death

Primary producers　　　　**Herbivores**　　**Carnivores**

AN ESTUARY ECOSYSTEM *(left)* **is richly supplied with nutrients delivered by the river and tides. These support a large population of invertebrate animals, which provide food for wading birds.**

As well as grasses the estuary supports algae (relatively simple plants—the group includes seaweeds). The sea lettuce (*Ulva lactuca*), with its delicate fronds, is common. The fronds of *Cladophora sericea* are bushy, and those of *Chaetomorpha linum* are like blades of grass.

Living in the Mud

Down in the mud of the estuary it is dark and airless as well as salty. These conditions are ideal for those bacteria that can live only in airless conditions. The upper layers of mud can contain over 1,000 times more bacteria than the water above the mud. There are often between 2.8 billion and 11.4 billion bacteria in one ounce of mud (100–400 million per gram).

Not many animals can cope with this environment, but for those that can the rewards are great, because the mud is rich in nutrients—including those produced by the bacteria and the bacteria themselves. Consequently, estuarine muds support only a few species of invertebrate animals, but members of those species are usually present in vast numbers.

Where the water is brackish, with a salinity of 5–18‰, there are lugworms (*Nereis* species), oysters, clams, crabs, and shrimps. On the seaward side of this region, where the water is saltier, there are marine species that are able to tolerate low salinity. On the upstream side, where the water is fresher, there are freshwater species able to tolerate slightly brackish conditions—salinity no higher than about 5‰.

The invertebrates feed in different ways. There are barnacles (*Gammarus* species) that graze the algae and other animals that feed on fragments of organic material and the bacteria and other organisms clinging to them. Clams and spire shells (*Hydrobia* species) feed in this way, as do some tiny crustaceans, such as *Corophium linearis*. Only about one-third of an inch (8.5 mm) long, this animal looks like a shrimp and lives in a short, U-shaped tube in the mud or sand. Oysters filter the water for the edible particles it contains. Predators include the lugworms and shore crabs (*Callinectes* species).

At high tide, when the surface is covered, fish feed on the invertebrates. Plaice (*Pleuronectes platessa*) eat worms, for example, and flounders (*Platichthys flesus*) prefer crustaceans. Skates and rays (members of the order Rajiformes of cartilaginous fish) also feed in estuaries. Rays forage by excavating shallow depressions to find food.

Wading Birds

At low tide, when the fish have gone and the sand and mud are exposed, birds arrive to feed. Shore birds forage along the edge of the water and in the zone between the low and high tide lines. Because they seek food near the edge of

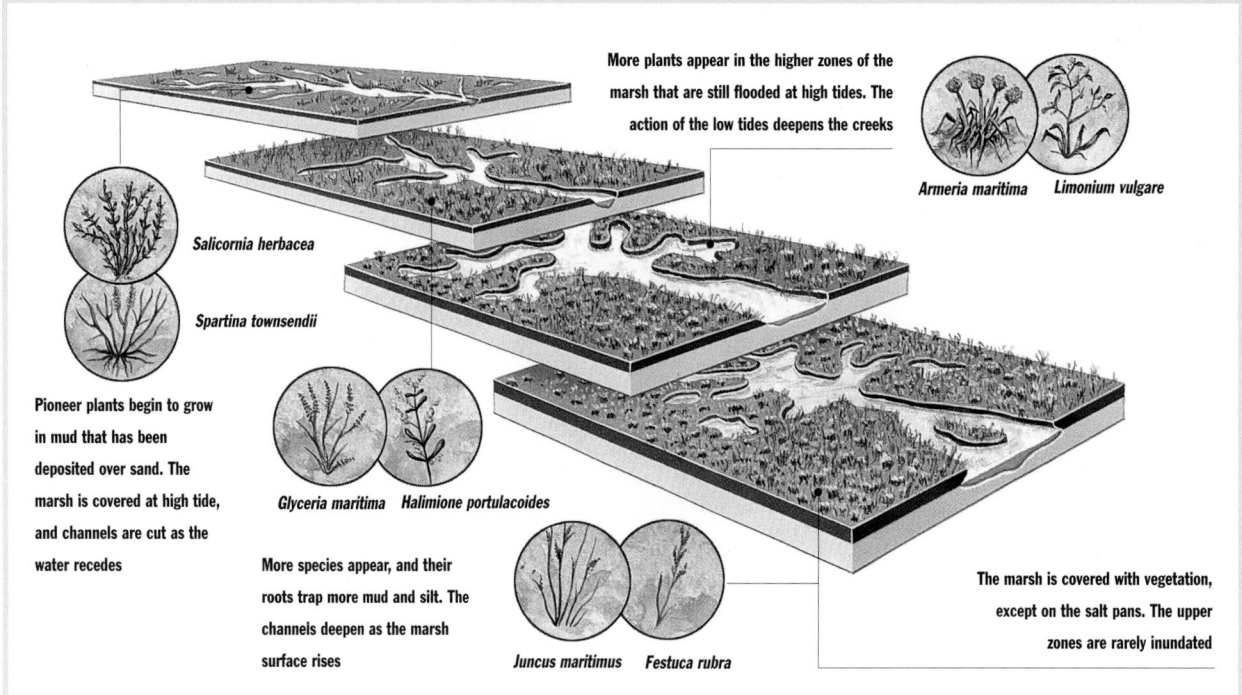

More plants appear in the higher zones of the marsh that are still flooded at high tides. The action of the low tides deepens the creeks

Armeria maritima   *Limonium vulgare*

Salicornia herbacea

Spartina townsendii

Pioneer plants begin to grow in mud that has been deposited over sand. The marsh is covered at high tide, and channels are cut as the water recedes

Glyceria maritima   *Halimione portulacoides*

More species appear, and their roots trap more mud and silt. The channels deepen as the marsh surface rises

Juncus maritimus   *Festuca rubra*

The marsh is covered with vegetation, except on the salt pans. The upper zones are rarely inundated

THE DEVELOPMENT OF A EUROPEAN SALT MARSH *(above)* **begins in a sheltered creek or bay in mud that is exposed at low tide. Conditions are harsh, and only a few species are able to tolerate them. Eventually, the surface of the salt marsh may be raised beyond the reach of all but the highest tides.**

SEA LAVENDER *(Limonium* **species)** *(opposite)* **is a salt-marsh plant that accumulates salt in its leaves. When these are shed, the plant rids itself of excess salt. Its seeds will not germinate unless they are exposed to seawater.**

the water, they are often called wading birds or simply waders. They vary in size, the length of their legs determining how far into the water they are able to venture. The great white, or common, egret (*Egretta alba*) has very long legs. It feeds mainly on fish, catching them by standing very still in the water and seizing them as they pass.

The turnstone, or ruddy turnstone (*Arenaria interpres*), earns its name from its method, which is to turn over stones and catch whatever small animal may lurk beneath. Small flocks of sanderlings (*Calidris alba*) feed on mollusks and crustaceans they catch right at the water's edge by running after a wave as it retreats, plucking mollusks from just below the surface, then running back up the shore again ahead of the incoming wave.

On the mudflats and sandbanks some of the wading birds forage on the surface, but most probe for the invertebrate animals that live

buried in the sand and mud. Their bills are of different lengths and shapes. This allows them to specialize because each invertebrate species inhabits a particular depth.

Oystercatchers (*Haematopus ostralegus*) eat worms, crabs, and oysters and mussels they are able to break open with their strong, straight bills. Snowy plovers (*Charadrius alexandrinus*) have very short bills. They will eat mollusks such as spire shells that live close to the surface. The whimbrel (*Numenius phaeopus*) has a long, curved bill that allows it to dig more deeply than most waders for the worms, mollusks, and crustaceans on which it feeds. It is closely related to the somewhat larger curlew (*N. arquata*), which feeds in the same fashion.

Salt Marshes

Salt marshes are transitional areas between the sea and dry land, often in sheltered bays and creeks along coasts, or along the edges of an

estuary. They occur along most of the coasts of North America, northwestern Europe, Japan, Korea, and New Zealand, as well as in parts of temperate South America and Australia.

Like the mud of the estuary, the salt marsh is a harsh environment. At high tide the marsh is flooded with seawater. Then, when the tide retreats, large mud flats may be exposed. If the sun is shining, evaporation will rapidly result in a very saline environment. Heavy rain at low tide can reduce the salinity almost to that of fresh water. Below the surface the mud is very salty at all times—and it is airless.

Equally significantly, plants living in the salt marsh must tolerate frequent and often large changes in temperature around their roots. In summer the air temperature, to which they are exposed at low tide, may be about 75°F (24°C), and the sea temperature, to which they are exposed at high tide, about 50°F (10°C). In winter the air temperature may be below freezing, while the sea, which has been warming all through the summer, is about 54°F (12°C).

The most important species are cord grasses of the genus *Spartina*. Their leaves have salt glands that secrete almost pure salt, ridding the plant of excess salt. This washes away in the rain. On dry days the salt crystallizes as a fine powder that blows away. They have thick stems and root systems that trap and bind mud brought in by the tides. As they will grow on bare mud, they are often the first plants to arrive, or "colonize," the mud. *Spartina* grow on salt marshes throughout the world.

Rushes (*Juncus* species) are also common. As with cord grasses, tall species of rushes grow at the lower levels, and shorter species farther from the water. Other common plants are sea lavender (*Limonium californicum*) and spike grass (*Distichlis spicata*).

Animals also find the conditions difficult. The only residents are insects and snails, which

A RIVER SWAMP ECOSYSTEM, in this case in tropical Africa. The primary producers are algae and floating or rooted plants.

Components of the ecosystem

1 Papyrus
2 Reeds
3 Water cabbage
4 Algae
5 Detritus
6 Crustaceans browsing on algae
7 Swamp worm
8 Hippopotamus
9 Sitatunga
10 Water snail
11 Nile perch
12 Malachite kingfisher
13 Saddlebilled stork
14 African spoonbill
15 Tilapia

Energy flow

⇨ Primary producer/primary consumer
⇨ Primary/secondary consumer
⇨ Secondary/tertiary consumer
⇨ Dead material/decomposer
⇨ Death

Primary producers   **Herbivores**   **Carnivores**

Sonneratia pokes up pneumatophores through the mud at the edge of the mangrove swamp where the trees are regularly inundated by the sea

Rhizophora produces a tangle of prop roots that, like the pneumatophores, help the tree to breathe. The aerial roots trap mud brought in by the tide

Bruquiera, with kneelike breathing roots, is less tolerant of seawater and will only survive occasional flooding by very high tides

live above the surface, and mollusks, shrimps, and crabs, which bury themselves in the mud. Snails and insects are not aquatic so they can live anywhere in the marsh. Mollusks, such as periwinkles and mussels, and crustaceans, such as shrimps and crabs, live on the saltier, seaward side of the marsh.

LIFE IN SWAMPS

In swamps several species of trees grow, sometimes as forests. In parts of the northern United States, tamarack (*Larix laricina*), black spruce (*Picea mariana*), and white cedar (*Thuja occidentalis*) grow in river swamps. In the eastern states the trees are elms (*Ulmus* species), ashes (*Fraxinus* species), maple (*Acer* species), and birches (*Betula* species). In the southern states freshwater swamps contain tupelo gum (*Nyssa aquatica*) and water gum (*N. biflora*).

Tropical Freshwater Swamps

Over much of tropical Africa the most abundant plant in freshwater swamps is papyrus, or paper, reed (*Cyperus papyrus*). There are similar swamps in South America, where other types of reed predominate.

Papyrus swamps cover about 3,900 square miles (10,000 sq. km) in East Africa. In southern Sudan papyrus is the predominant plant in an area of wetland fed by tributaries of the White Nile that is about 200 miles (320 km) long and 225 miles (360 km) wide. Its Arabic name is *Sudd*. Only small, shallow-draft boats can sail through it.

Papyrus reeds grow up to 10 feet (3 m) tall, and they tend to exclude other plants. They are rooted in the mud, however, so they do not compete with floating plants that need no contact with the bottom and can grow in deeper water. Water hyacinth (*Eichhornia crassipes*) has colonized the open water. This is a fast-growing

MANGROVE TREE ROOTS. Mangroves fringe coastlines in tropical and subtropical regions. Different species of mangroves have different specialized roots that allow them to grow in waterlogged, airless ground.

plant native to South America that is now considered a serious weed in rivers and lakes throughout the tropics.

Plant growth is rapid in the warm climate, and there is an abundance of food for animals. Worms, mollusks, and crustaceans feed on algae or particles they find in the mud, and fishes and birds feed on them. In places the *Sudd* is shallow enough for elephants to cross it, and there are crocodiles and hippopotamuses in the deeper parts.

Mangrove Swamps

On tropical and subtropical coasts swamps take the place of salt marshes. These are wetlands that support trees, but the water is salty, and the trees are mangroves. A mangrove swamp is sometimes called a mangal.

Mangroves can grow only in very sheltered places. Strong waves would wash away their seeds before they were able to put down roots. Because there is so little movement in a mangrove swamp, any solid particles that wash into it tend to settle, and the mud accumulates around the mangrove roots. This makes the water shallower, allowing mangroves to grow a little farther from the shore, and little by little the coast is extended into the sea.

The trees themselves have to grow in waterlogged, salty mud, and mangroves have shallow, wide-spreading roots. Some species cope with the salt by secreting it from specialized cells in their leaves. The salt is washed away from those leaves low enough to touch the water at high tide and dries as a powdery coating on others, to be removed when these are shed. Other species are able to take

COASTAL CLIFFS provide nesting sites for many sea birds. These are kittiwakes *(Rissa tridactyla)*. They use guano (the droppings of seabirds) to stick their nests, made of seaweed, to the cliffs.

water into their roots without absorbing salt.

Roots must also be able to absorb oxygen for respiration. To achieve this, mangroves have developed many specialized root systems. Horizontal roots of species belonging to the genus *Sonneratia* run just below the surface and produce vertical extensions that project upward. These "peg roots," or "pneumatophores," stand above the water except at high tide, and *Sonneratia* mangroves grow right on the shore.

Rhizophora mangroves grow farther from the shore, where the tides do not rise so high. They produce a mass of "stilt," or "prop," roots.

Farthest of all from the sea, *Bruguiera* mangroves produce "knee" roots. These have loops that rise above the mud.

Cormorants (family Phalacrocoracidae) and herons, ibises, and anhingas (family Anhingidae), are among the many species of aquatic birds that nest in mangrove trees. The tree roots provide shelter for many animals, and the mud contains plant and animal remains on which they feed. Fiddler crabs (*Uca* species) are among the scavengers near the water's edge. At low tide mammals, such as raccoons (*Procyon lotor*) in the United States, also forage and hunt.

LIFE ON THE ROCKY SEA SHORE

Between sea and dry land and not wholly a part of either, the shore is not one environment but

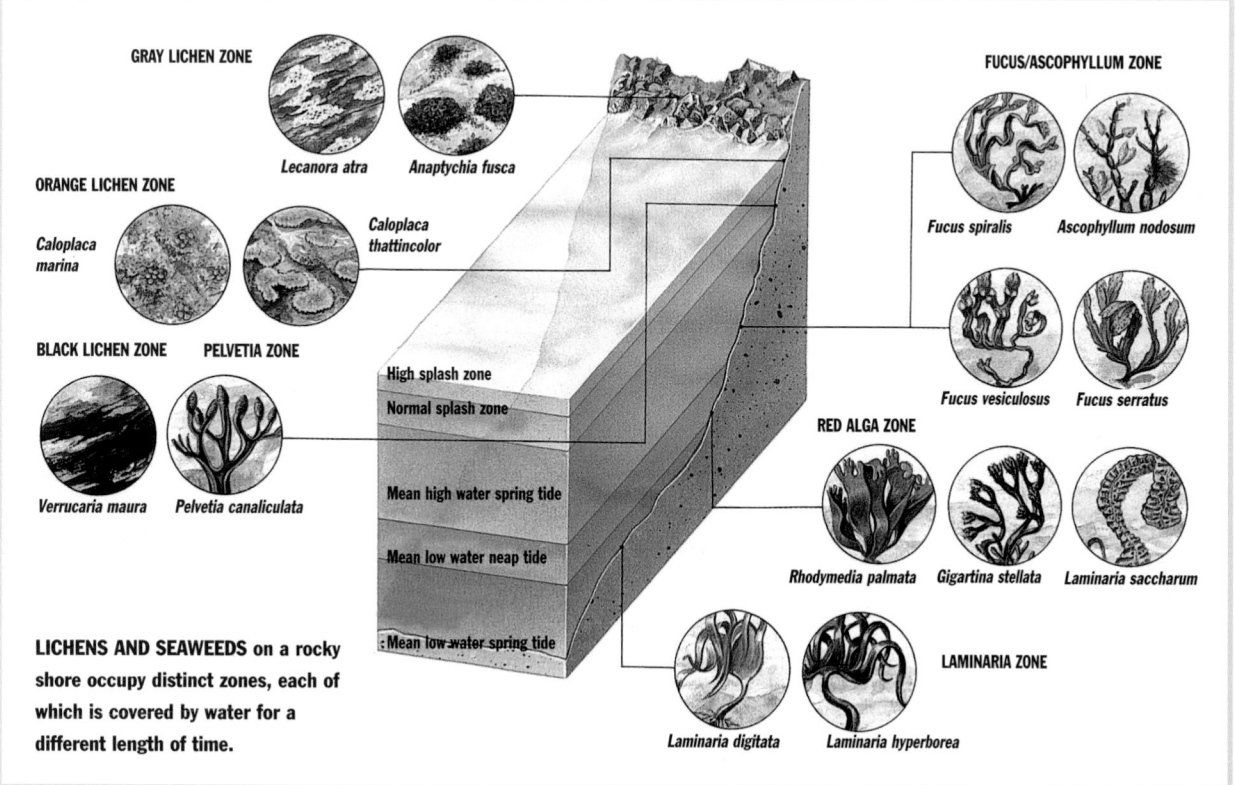

GRAY LICHEN ZONE

Lecanora atra   *Anaptychia fusca*

ORANGE LICHEN ZONE

Caloplaca marina   *Caloplaca thattincolor*

BLACK LICHEN ZONE   PELVETIA ZONE

Verrucaria maura   *Pelvetia canaliculata*

High splash zone
Normal splash zone
Mean high water spring tide
Mean low water neap tide
Mean low water spring tide

FUCUS/ASCOPHYLLUM ZONE

Fucus spiralis   *Ascophyllum nodosum*

Fucus vesiculosus   *Fucus serratus*

RED ALGA ZONE

Rhodymedia palmata   *Gigartina stellata*   *Laminaria saccharum*

LAMINARIA ZONE

Laminaria digitata   *Laminaria hyperborea*

LICHENS AND SEAWEEDS on a rocky shore occupy distinct zones, each of which is covered by water for a different length of time.

several, and each has its own inhabitants. At the deepest level there is a region that is covered by water even at the lowest tides. At the highest level there is a region the highest tides never reach. Bands within the intertidal zone, between these two extremes, are covered by water for varying lengths of time and with varying frequencies.

Plants and animals living on the shore have more than tides to contend with. Waves smash against the shore then rush back to the sea, in places with great force. Shores vary widely in the amount of wave energy to which they are exposed, but on some it is enough to dislodge most organisms. Those that manage to live there fix themselves so firmly to the rocks no wave can shift them. Limpets and barnacles grip so tightly they almost become part of the rocks on which they rest. Seaweeds are anchored no less securely with a structure called a holdfast.

Protected Areas

Some shores are protected from wave action. Most of the coast of the southeastern United States lies behind barrier islands. Long, narrow, and aligned parallel to the coast, barrier islands are made from sand deposited by currents. They protect the shore from all but the gentlest wave action, and especially from storms.

Coral reefs can have a similar sheltering effect. Some, such as the Great Barrier Reef off the Australian coast, form parallel to the shore and are called barrier reefs. Others, called fringing reefs, are attached to the shore and extend seaward from it. Both types absorb the energy of the waves, protecting the shore.

Atolls provide the greatest protection of all.

An atoll is a coral reef that grows around the edge of a sunken volcanic crater. The reef forms a circle with an area of sea enclosed within it. Sea that is partly isolated from the main ocean by a barrier or atoll is called a lagoon.

Plants of the Rocky Shore

Algae are the only plants living on the rocky shore. These are very simple plants, but this does not mean they are necessarily small. Seaweeds, known as wracks and kelps, are the biggest of them. Kelps belonging to the genus *Laminaria* have fronds up to 9 feet (3 m) long.

Lichens also grow on rocks on the shore. A lichen consists of a fungus living in close association with an alga or cyanobacterium. Cyanobacteria are bacteria that can manufacture sugars by photosynthesis. At one time they were classified as algae and called blue-green algae. Identifying lichens is not easy, but those found on the shore can be grouped by their colors. They cannot grow on rocks that are submerged frequently or for long.

Black lichens, such as *Verrucaria maura*, grow on rocks that are submerged by the highest tides. Orange lichens, such as *Caloplaca* species, grow a little higher, on rocks that are splashed by waves during very high tides. Gray lichens, such as *Anaptychia fusca* and *Lecanora atra*, grow higher still, where they are only occasionally splashed by waves. The part of the shore occupied by orange and gray lichens is called the supralittoral zone. ("Littoral" is from the Latin *litoralis*, meaning "shore.")

The limit for black lichens marks the upper

ANIMALS OF THE INTERTIDAL ZONE on a rocky shore in southern Africa. In the littoral fringe or splash zone, which is rarely covered by water, the sea slater can be found. On the upper eulittoral, which is only submerged at high tide, the periwinkle and acorn barnacles are found. On the mid-eulittoral, which is exposed to the air for about 12 hours in each 24 hours, the periwinkle, brown mussel, and limpets are found.

Tube worm
Pomatoleios crosslandi

Dead man's fingers
Alcyonium fallax

On the lower eulittoral, which is covered by sea for most of each day, the tube worm is found. In the sublittoral fringe, which is only very rarely exposed to the air, a soft coral called dead man's fingers and the sea squirt are found.

boundary of the next shore zone, called the eulittoral zone. It supports green seaweeds, such as *Pelvetia canaliculata*, growing just below the black lichens. They are submerged by only the highest tides. Brown seaweeds—wracks— growing below them, are always submerged at high tide, and in the lower part of the eulittoral zone they are under water even at the low tide. They include flat wrack (*Fucus spiralis*) and knotted wrack (*Ascophyllum nodosum*) in the higher part of the

zone and bladderwrack (*F. vesiculosus*) and serrated wrack (*F. serratus*)—named after the sawlike teeth on the edges of their fronds— below them. Some bladderwracks develop air pockets along their fronds. The function of these is not fully understood.

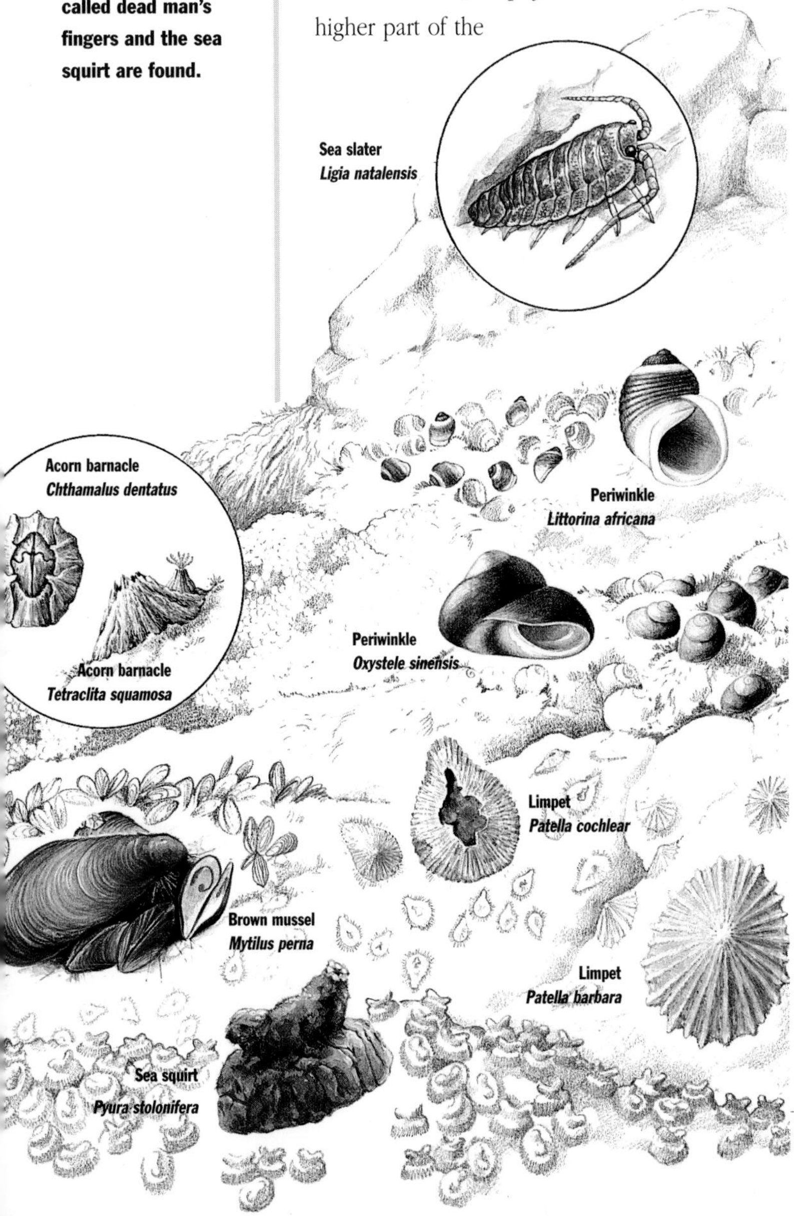

Farther down the shore there is the sublittoral fringe, a zone that is exposed only by very low tides. Red seaweeds, such as *Rhodymenia palmata,* grow there. They contain a red pigment that is able to use the diffused light that filters down to them in a more efficient way than the green or brown pigments of other seaweeds; therefore, they are able to photysynthesize at greater depths.

Most of the kelps grow in the sublittoral zone and are submerged at all times. If the rocky surface is fairly level, kelp forests may form, with the tall fronds of *Laminaria digitata*, *L. hyperbores*, and other species waving gently in the currents like trees in the wind.

Animals of the Rocky Shore

The small animals that live on the shore occupy particular areas according to the amount of time they are submerged or exposed.

The upper boundary of the supralittoral zone, farthest from the sea, marks the limit beyond which periwinkles of the genus *Littorina* will not move. Periwinkles are snails, and beyond their zone ordinary land snails are found. The presence of barnacles (*Balanus* species) marks the supralittoral zone's lower boundary.

Barnacles, including acorn barnacles (*Chthamalus* species), live in most of the eulittoral zone and the sublittoral fringe. In the mid-eulittoral zone limpets (*Patella* species) and

Sea slater
Ligia natalensis

Acorn barnacle
Chthamalus dentatus

Acorn barnacle
Tetraclita squamosa

Periwinkle
Littorina africana

Periwinkle
Oxystele sinensis

Limpet
Patella cochlear

Brown mussel
Mytilus perna

Limpet
Patella barbara

Sea squirt
Pyura stolonifera

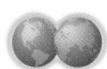

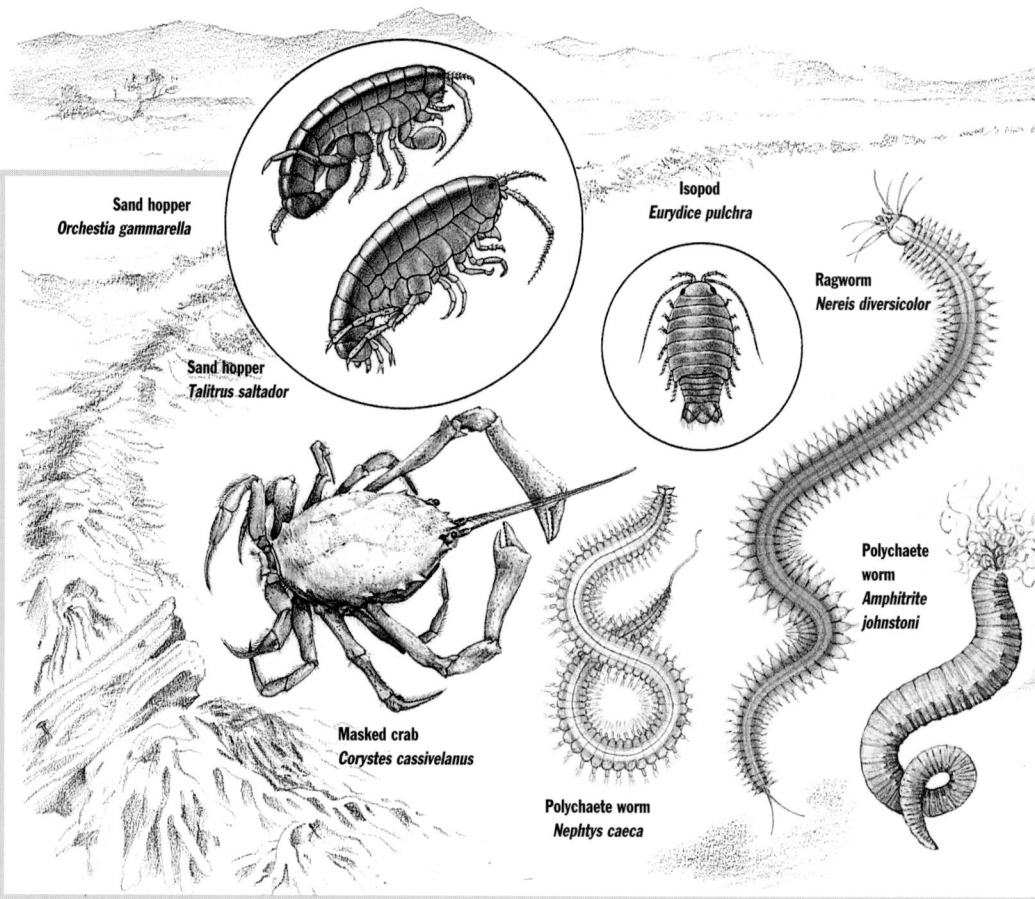

Sand hopper
Orchestia gammarella

Sand hopper
Talitrus saltador

Isopod
Eurydice pulchra

Ragworm
Nereis diversicolor

Polychaete worm
Amphitrite johnstoni

Masked crab
Corystes cassivelanus

Polychaete worm
Nephtys caeca

mussels (*Mytilus* species) can be found. The sublittoral zone, which is rarely exposed to air, is inhabited by soft-bodied marine animals such as the colonies of soft corals known as dead man's fingers (*Alcyonium* species) and sea squirts (*Pyura* species).

Rock Pools

The hollows and depressions in rocky shores are often filled with water. These pools vary in area and depth, but most contain a variety of plants and animals, including gastropods (snail-like mollusks) such as the common limpet (*Patella vulgata*), which clings to the rock with its muscular foot.

Rock pools look like ideal places for marine organisms to shelter at low tide, but they also present challenges. While isolated from the sea, the water in a pool will warm or cool depending on the season and the weather. The bigger the pool, the longer its temperature takes to change, but on a hot day the temperature in a small pool may rise high enough to kill most of the organisms in it. On a cold day the water may almost freeze at low tide. Then, as the tide returns, the temperature abruptly changes to that of the sea.

Heating causes water to evaporate; when water evaporates, salts dissolved in it are left behind. In hot weather the salinity rises sharply in a rock pool. Salinity may fall if a heavy downpour of rain adds fresh water to the pool. Oxygen levels also vary. Cold water can hold more dissolved oxygen than warm water. As a

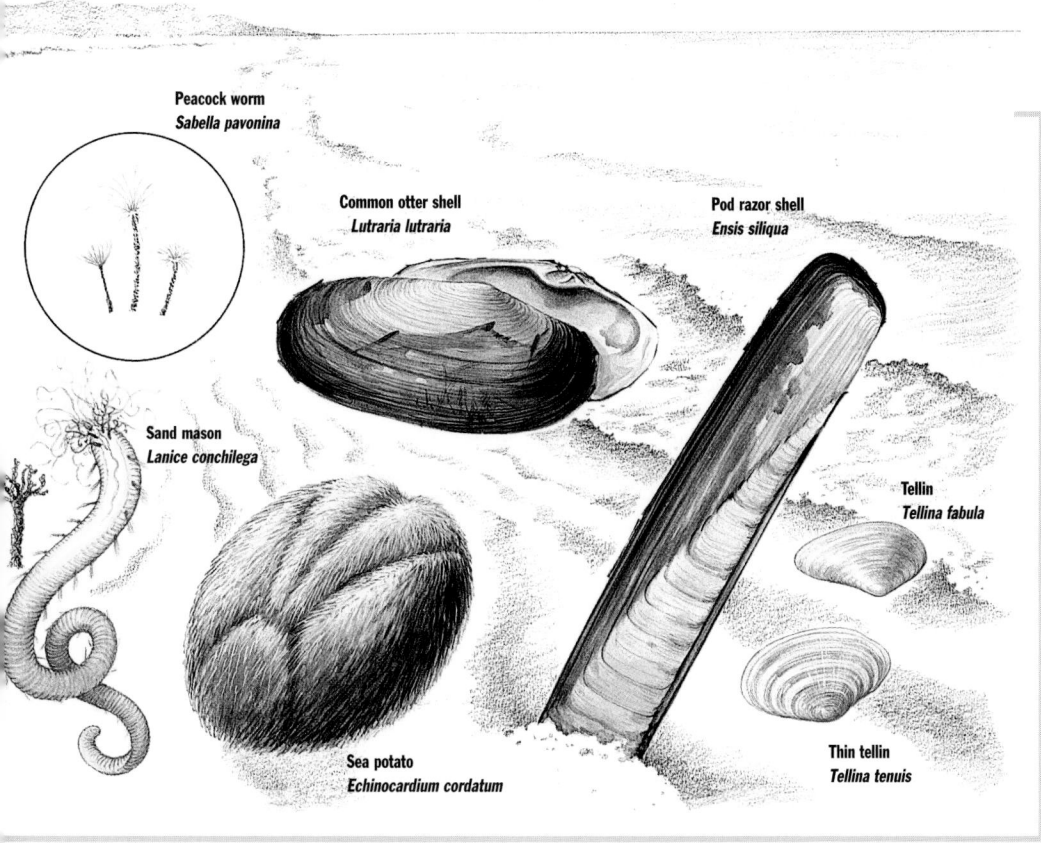

Peacock worm
Sabella pavonina

Common otter shell
Lutraria lutraria

Pod razor shell
Ensis siliqua

Sand mason
Lanice conchilega

Tellin
Tellina fabula

Sea potato
Echinocardium cordatum

Thin tellin
Tellina tenuis

ANIMALS OF SANDY SHORE in northwestern Europe. Along the strandline, where seaweed and other debris are deposited by the tide, there are sand hoppers. On the upper shore is the masked crab, the polychaete worm *Nephtys caeca*, and an isopod. On the mid-shore there is the ragworm, polychaete worms such as *Amphitrite johnstoni*, the sand mason, and the peacock worm. On the lower shore and continuous shallow water there is the sea potato, common otter shell, pod razor shell, and tellins.

pool warms, its ability to hold oxygen decreases.

A large, deep pool often contains some species of green seaweed, such as sea lettuce (*Ulva lactuca*) and *Codium fragile*. There are also sea anemones, which have tiny stinging cells in their tentacles to paralyze their prey. The dahlia anemone (*Tealia felina*) is one of the larger species, measuring up to 2 inches (5 cm) in diameter.

Prawns (*Palaemon serratus*) and common shore crabs (*Carcinus maenas*) also inhabit rock pools. They are scavengers, eating both plants and small animals. Small fish and many species of starfish eat the mollusks and worms that feed on the plants.

Gobies and blennies are the most abundant fishes. In Europe the commonest, the blenny (*Blennis pholis*), is called a shanny. On American coasts from North Carolina to Brazil it is the redlip blenny (*Ophioblennius atlanticus*). Many pools contain the common goby (*Gobius minutus*) and rock goby (*G. paganellus*).

LIFE ON SANDY SHORES

Beaches are made and then altered by the action of waves. As a wave breaks, water runs up the shore. This is called swash; it carries particles that are then dropped. The flow of water back toward the sea (backwash) also carries particles.

A beach formed by strong waves—a "high-energy beach"—slopes steeply and consists of pebbles, gravel, and coarse sand. The waves

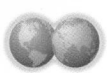

throw material onto the shore, the swash carries it forward, and the weaker backwash carries away the fine particles. The remaining particles are large, and water drains from them quickly, so at low tide the beach soon becomes very dry. This makes it a difficult environment for marine animals to live in. Very few animals live on high-energy beaches.

Gentle waves have a very different effect. Fine particles are washed a short distance up the beach, and only a small proportion of them are returned by the backwash. The beach slopes fairly gently and is made from fine sand. Water tends to cling to sand grains, filling the spaces between them, and this kind of beach dries out much more slowly. It is a much better environment for marine animals.

Most of the inhabitants of a sandy beach bury themselves at low tide—it is easier to burrow in wet sand than in dry sand. This prevents them from drying out and also protects them from predators, such as birds. The beach looks empty only because the animals are out of sight. If they are disturbed, they rapidly bury themselves again.

Sand hoppers shelter beneath seaweed. When disturbed they scatter, hopping through the sand in search of cover. They are crustaceans—related to crabs and lobsters despite looking so different—and there are several species. Isopods are also crustaceans and resemble woodlice, to which they are related. When the tide submerges the beach, they emerge and swim vigorously. They are small animals, females of *Eurydice pulchra* being about 0.25 inches (6 mm) long, and the males half that size. Crabs also shelter in the wet sand.

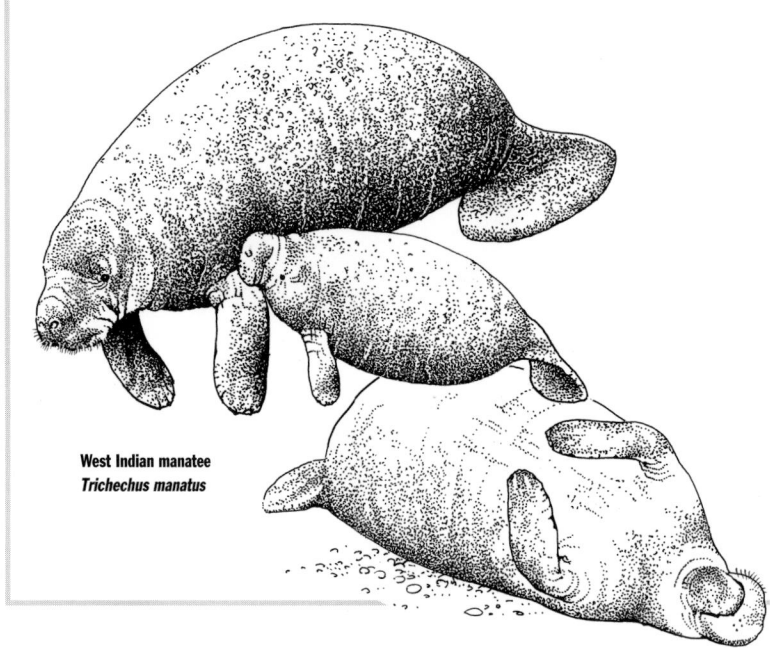

West Indian manatee
Trichechus manatus

Seashells that litter beaches may have been washed ashore, but some belong to animals that live on the beach itself. Razor shells (*Ensis ensis*) and pod razors (*E. siliqua*) are easy to recognize, and the common otter shell (*Lutraria lutraria*) is also familiar. These are bivalve mollusks, that is, their shells (called valves) have two parts.

SEA COWS

Dugongs and manatees are mammals comprising the order Sirenia. They are related to horses, elephants, and rhinoceroses. They are often called sea cows. Despite having a similar streamlined body shape to other marine mammals such as seals and sea lions, they are quite different. Because sea cows sometimes adopt a rather upright stance, they are believed to be the origin of the idea of mermaids.

WEST INDIAN MANATEES *(above)* inhabit shallow, coastal waters, estuaries and rivers from Florida to central Brazil. They breed slowly and suckle their young (calves) for 12 to 18 months. Here a mother and her calf are shown *(top)*. They sometimes lie on their backs *(bottom)*.

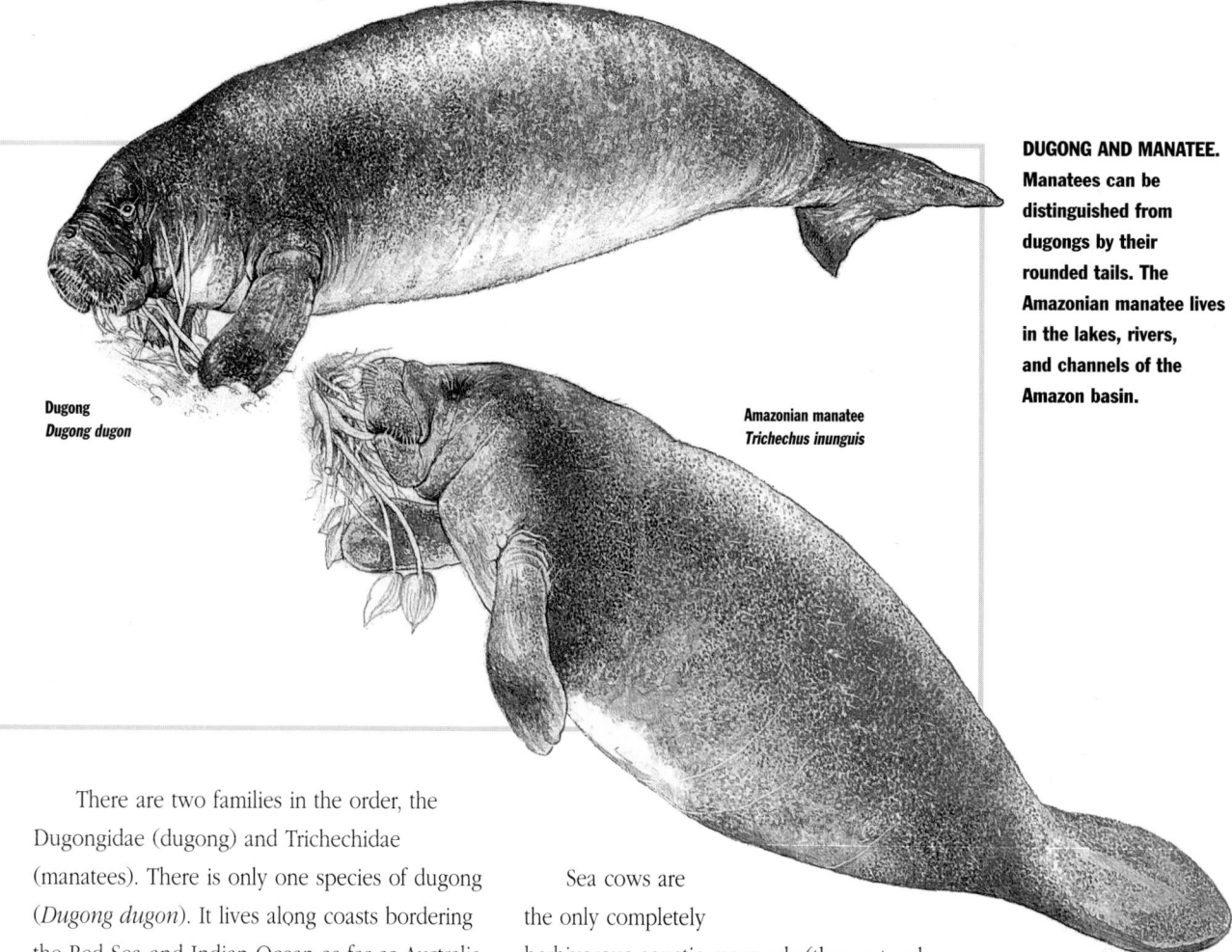

Dugong
Dugong dugon

Amazonian manatee
Trichechus inunguis

DUGONG AND MANATEE.
Manatees can be distinguished from dugongs by their rounded tails. The Amazonian manatee lives in the lakes, rivers, and channels of the Amazon basin.

There are two families in the order, the Dugongidae (dugong) and Trichechidae (manatees). There is only one species of dugong (*Dugong dugon*). It lives along coasts bordering the Red Sea and Indian Ocean as far as Australia. Its nostrils are on the top of its muzzle, allowing it to breathe without fully surfacing.

There are three species of manatees. The West Indian manatee (*Trichechus manatus*) inhabits waters from Florida to central Brazil. The Amazonian manatee (*T. inunguis*) lives in the Amazon basin. The West African manatee (*T. senegalensis*) lives off the West African coast from Senegal to Angola.

Sea cows are bulky animals because of the thick layer of fat (blubber) beneath the skin. Adults are up to about 10 feet (3 m) long (although the West Indian manatee is bigger). They have small eyes and small holes as ear openings.

Sea cows are the only completely herbivorous aquatic mammals (they eat only plants). They occupy a unique feeding niche; that is, they have no significant competitors (sea turtles are the only large herbivores with a similar diet). They can eat an enormous quantity of marine vegetation, and Amazonian manatees have been used to clear waterways of weeds.

The West Indian manatee has small "nails" on its flippers. These serve no purpose but are inherited from the land-dwelling ancestor of all the sea cows. Manatees seize food with their enlarged, strong, and very flexible upper lip. They have no teeth at the front of their mouths, but their gums are very tough. Dugongs have a tough pad on the lower jaw and small teeth in the upper jaw.

Survival of the Wetlands

*L*ow-lying and waterlogged, wetlands appear unattractive and useless to many people. The sites they occupy are valuable, however. Coastal plains and the flood plains of rivers are attractive places to live. This has led to the draining of many wetlands and the loss of the valuable wildlife they support. Wetlands are also vulnerable to water-borne pollution.

THE EVERGLADES in Florida *(opposite)*. Much of this subtropical wetland has been drained for cultivation and to build homes and roads. The area was classified as a protected wilderness in 1976. What remains of it is now being restored.

RECLAIMED LAND IN THE NETHERLANDS. Farmers rely on dikes to prevent their land being flooded by the sea. In 1932 the Afsluitdijk was built across part of the former Zuider Zee, and some of the enclosed land was drained. The remainder is a freshwater lake called the IJsselmeer.

Along the Atlantic coast of the United States, from North Carolina to Florida, and around the coast of the Gulf of Mexico, the land is level and low-lying. A warm climate and proximity to the sea have drawn many Americans to make their homes on the coastal strip. Since 1930 the

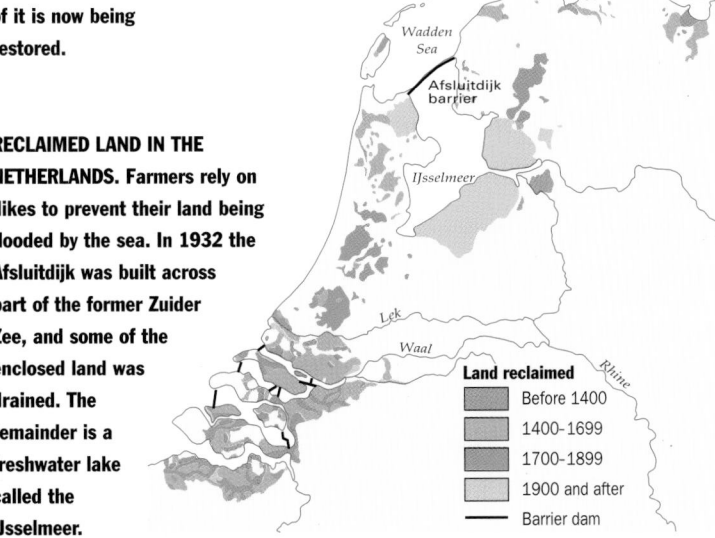

Wadden Sea

Afsluitdijk barrier

IJsselmeer

Lek

Waal

Rhine

Land reclaimed
- Before 1400
- 1400–1699
- 1700–1899
- 1900 and after
- Barrier dam

population there has almost doubled, and many of the new inhabitants live in mobile homes.

Parts of the coastal strip were wetlands, and, like coastal wetlands in many other parts of the world, they were drained for conversion to residential use or to provide hotels and other tourist amenities. There are dangers in living on low-lying ground near the coast or on the floodplain of a river. From time to time these areas are flooded; although sea walls can protect homes on the coast and high banks—levees—can be built to protect people living on flood plains, scientists now believe these measures sometimes divert floods to unprotected areas.

POLDERS

Many of the lands around the North Sea are low-lying. There is a tradition in Belgium and elsewhere of protecting them from encroachment by the sea and of developing ways of reclaiming the land. But it is the Dutch who are most famous for their stretches of reclaimed land—"polders"—and the windmills that were traditionally used to drain them.

When the sea began to flood across what were then low-lying marshes—wetlands—the inhabitants started building dikes to protect themselves and their land. The first polders were formed by this means more than 1,000 years ago, and the area of reclaimed land has continued to increase. In 1986 the Netherlands designated a new province, Flevoland, that consisted of two adjoining polders reclaimed from the IJsselmeer. Flevoland has an area of 551 square miles (272,800 sq. km), a population

(in 1996) of 272,800, and a capital city, Lelystad.

This type of reclamation does not necessarily involve losing wetland. It can also create it. In the north of the Netherlands, the West Friesian Islands (Westfriesche Eilanden) partly enclose an area of sea that was formerly called the Zuider Zee. In 1932 a barrier 19 miles (31 km) long, the IJsselmeer dam, was built across it. This completely enclosed the area south of the Dam. What remained of the Zuider Zee to the north is now called the Wadden Zee, and the southern part is the IJsselmeer, with an area of 1,425 square miles (3,691 sq. km). Most of the IJsselmeer is a shallow, freshwater lake, but about 40 percent of the original area has been reclaimed and converted to arable (crop-producing) land. The lake is an important habitat for migrating water birds.

The Incursion of Salt Water

Polders lie close to or below sea level. Making them begins with the construction of the dike that encloses the area to be reclaimed. On the outside of the dike there is a drainage canal to convey water to the sea. Water is then pumped out of the polder, traditionally using power from windmills but nowadays with pumps driven by diesel engines. Soon after the surface of the mud is exposed, plants tolerant of the high salinity start to grow naturally upon it. Fresh water is pumped onto the mud. It drains through the mud and is carried away to the sea, washing salt from the soil.

When the surface is dry enough, rushes and reeds are sown on it, and after three years the reeds are burned. This removes the remaining salt, the land is dry enough to plow, and the first ordinary farm crops can be sown. From start to finish the process takes seven years.

The reclaimed land is very fertile, but the sea is never far away. Some of the fresh water from the washing out of the salt accumulates below the surface as groundwater. Water from the rain and from adjacent land drains

CREATING A POLDER takes seven years. The operation begins with the building of a dike around the land to be reclaimed, then the water is removed. After that the excess salt must be removed from the soil.

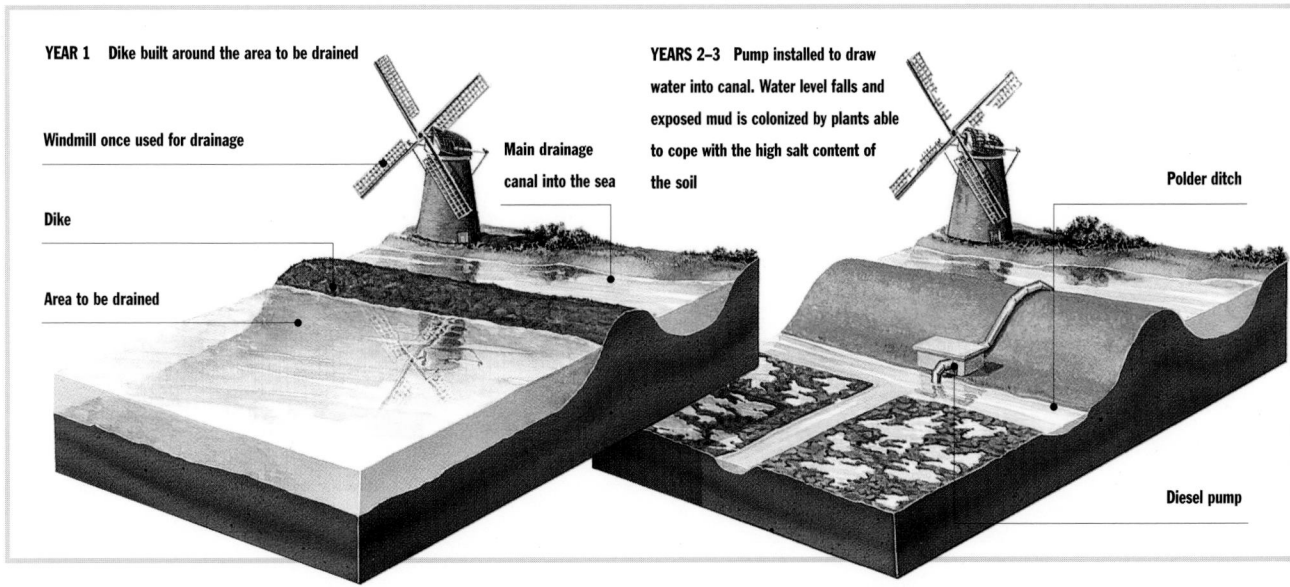

YEAR 1 Dike built around the area to be drained

Windmill once used for drainage

Dike

Area to be drained

Main drainage canal into the sea

YEARS 2–3 Pump installed to draw water into canal. Water level falls and exposed mud is colonized by plants able to cope with the high salt content of the soil

Polder ditch

Diesel pump

downward to join it. Water for crop irrigation is taken out from the groundwater. This reduces the amount of fresh water. The groundwater layer becomes thinner, and a wedge of denser, saltier water moves inland beneath the retreating fresh water. If it is left unchecked, the intrusion of salt water will poison the land.

The Dutch have solved this problem. Where a coastal polder was at risk, they isolated part of it by building a dike on the landward side. Then the enclosed area was flooded with fresh water. This created a new freshwater lake—a wetland area—and at the same time the weight of the fresh water pushed back the intruding sea water, protecting the fields farther inland.

The Dutch polders are famous, but similar ones are found in many parts of the world. There are farms on land reclaimed from the sea in most of the countries around the southern part of the North Sea, as well as in Japan, India, and several South American countries. Polders were made in Georgia and the Carolinas in the 18th

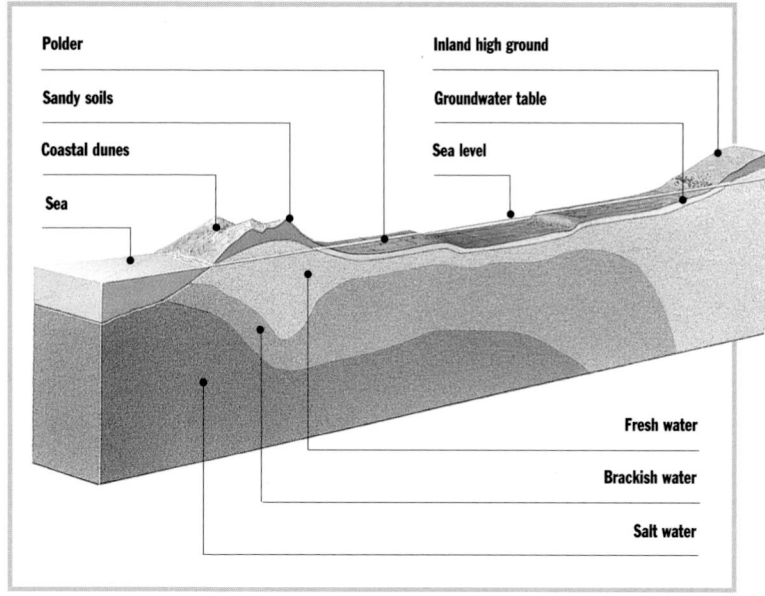

century. They were used mainly for growing rice. Eventually, they were abandoned and became coastal marshes.

POLLUTION

Rivers are fed by a constant flow of water draining from surrounding land. Ordinarily, this

SALTWATER INCURSION occurs when too much fresh water is abstracted for irrigation, lowering the water table and allowing a wedge of denser salt water to advance inland. The problem has been recognized since the 1950s in the United States. It affects every state with a coastline.

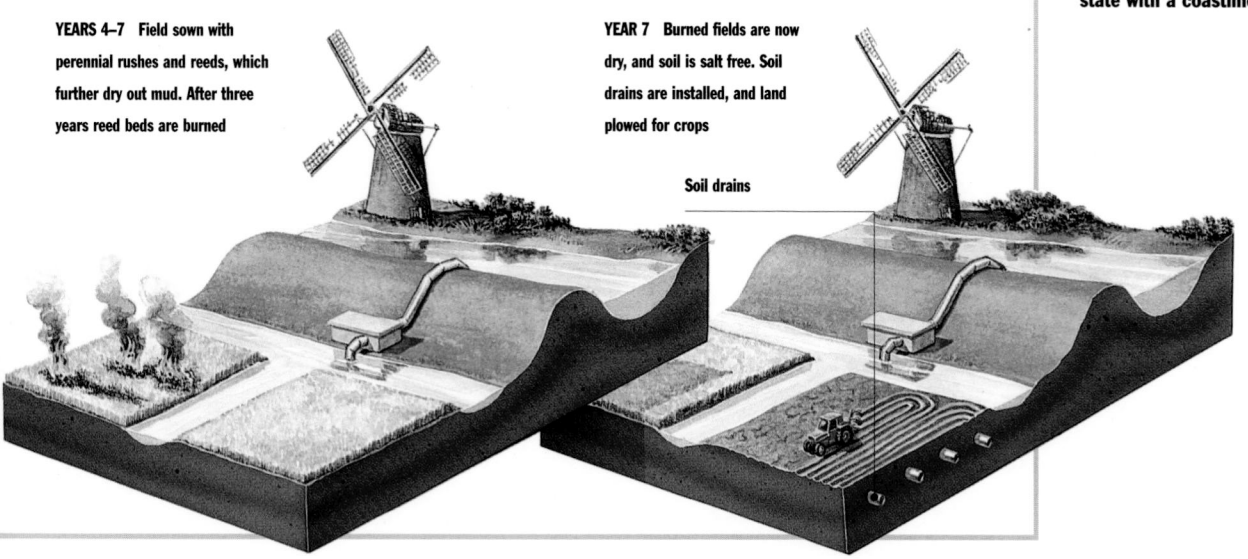

YEARS 4–7 Field sown with perennial rushes and reeds, which further dry out mud. After three years reed beds are burned

YEAR 7 Burned fields are now dry, and soil is salt free. Soil drains are installed, and land plowed for crops

Soil drains

means any harmful substance entering the water is rapidly removed and diluted. The damage it causes is localized, and water a short distance downstream is not affected. Rivers cleanse themselves very efficiently.

Their self-cleansing capacity can be overwhelmed, however. Some harmful substances—pollutants—are so poisonous that very small concentrations will kill most aquatic organisms, so they remain dangerous even when diluted. Others are less poisonous, but enter the river in very large amounts. They may also enter the river constantly. This used to happen in most industrial regions, where factories discharged their liquid wastes into the nearest river; there were many rivers in which nothing could live.

Today factories are not permitted to discharge into rivers any substance that can harm living organisms. Safe ways have been found for disposing of dangerous wastes, and industrial processes are now much more efficient than those of the past. This means that they make better use of energy and materials, and produce fewer wastes.

Eutrophication

Rivers and lakes are fed by water draining from farmland and may also receive water from sewage treatment plants. In both cases the water may contain plant nutrients, especially nitrates and phosphates. These stimulate the growth of aquatic plants, which can be beneficial. If there

EUTROPHICATION is the over-enrichment of water with plant nutrients. In extreme cases it can cause the death by asphyxiation of fish and most invertebrate animals.

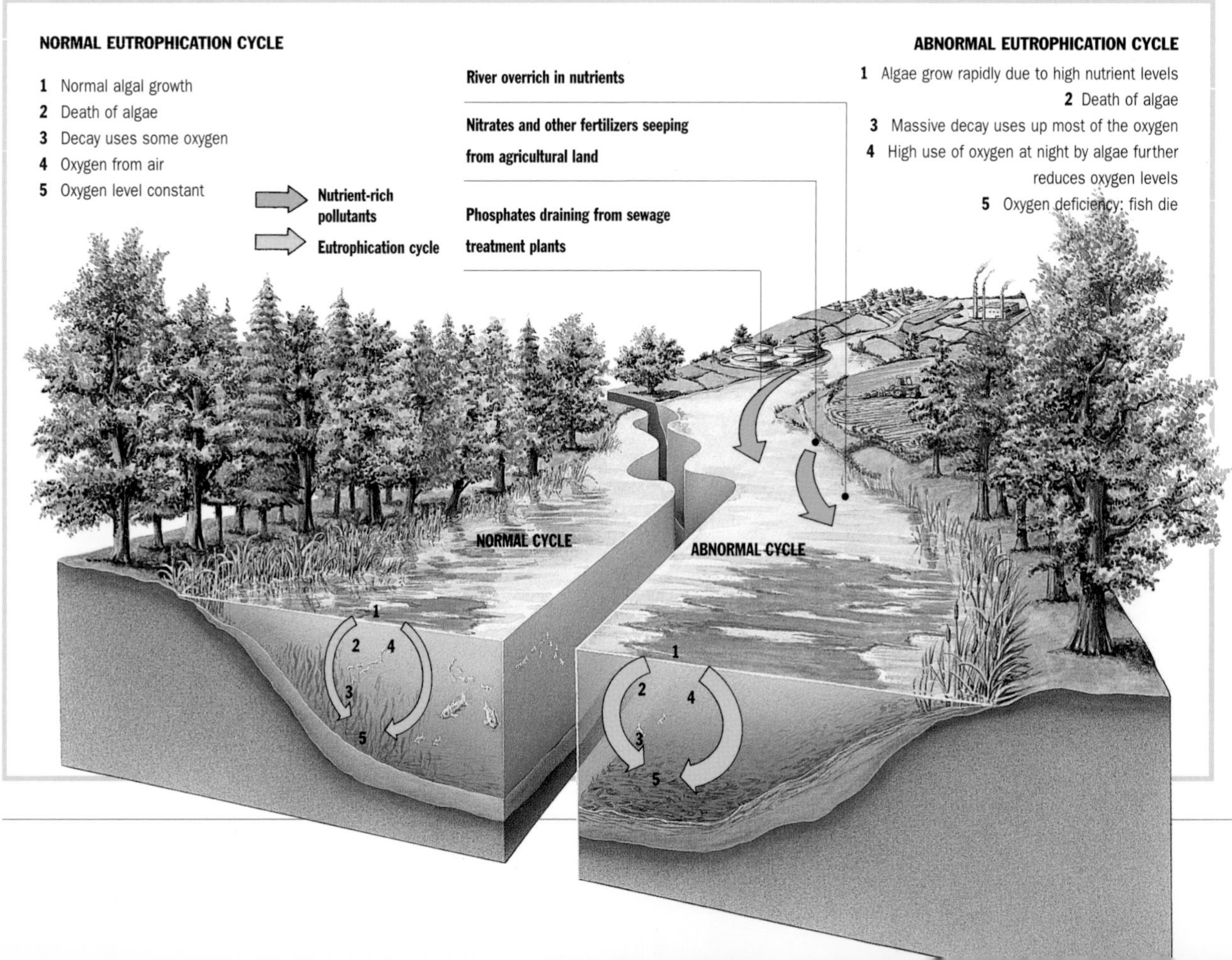

NORMAL EUTROPHICATION CYCLE

1 Normal algal growth
2 Death of algae
3 Decay uses some oxygen
4 Oxygen from air
5 Oxygen level constant

→ Nutrient-rich pollutants
→ Eutrophication cycle

River overrich in nutrients

Nitrates and other fertilizers seeping from agricultural land

Phosphates draining from sewage treatment plants

ABNORMAL EUTROPHICATION CYCLE

1 Algae grow rapidly due to high nutrient levels
2 Death of algae
3 Massive decay uses up most of the oxygen
4 High use of oxygen at night by algae further reduces oxygen levels
5 Oxygen deficiency; fish die

NORMAL CYCLE

ABNORMAL CYCLE

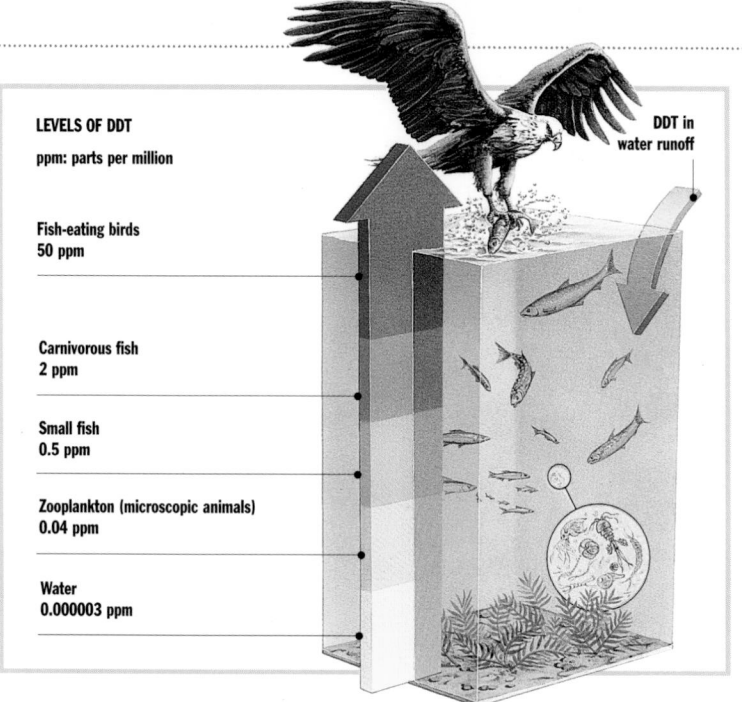

LEVELS OF DDT

ppm: parts per million

Fish-eating birds
50 ppm

Carnivorous fish
2 ppm

Small fish
0.5 ppm

Zooplankton (microscopic animals)
0.04 ppm

Water
0.000003 ppm

DDT in
water runoff

DDT IN THE FOOD CHAIN.
Insecticides such as DDT
can accumulate along
food chains until
predators such as fish,
eagles, and other birds
of prey receive doses
high enough to reduce
their capacity to
reproduce. DDT has now
been banned in some
countries.

are more plants, there can be more animals, and the community living in the river or lake becomes richer.

In excessive amounts, however, plant nutrients are harmful. The water containing them becomes "eutrophic"—meaning "over-enriched." The process by which the quality of the water deteriorates is called eutrophication. It most often occurs in still or slow-moving water because that is where nutrients can accumulate faster than the flow of water can dilute and remove them.

The nutrients stimulate plant growth, and the plants that can grow fastest are the ones that benefit most. These are the single-celled algae. Most are too small to see without a microscope, but there are so many they color the water, coat stones with a green slime, and form a scum on the surface.

Individual algae die, and others replace them. Those that die decompose through the action of bacteria in the water. The bacteria multiply rapidly in the presence of such an abundance of food, and before long the water contains vast numbers of algae and bacteria.

Both use oxygen, which they take from the water. The amount of dissolved oxygen falls. Fish and other animals asphyxiate and are then decomposed, using still more oxygen, and eventually the water supports only a very few types of organisms.

Biological Amplification

Some substances are only slightly poisonous, but chemically very stable. Released into the environment, they remain unchanged for a long time. Certain compounds of hydrogen, carbon, and chlorine—called organochlorines— are of this type. The insecticide dichlorodiphenyltrichloroethane, known as DDT, is an organochlorine, and so are substances called polychlorinated biphenyls (PCBs) that were formerly used for electrical insulation.

A small organism—say a worm—might consume some of one of these compounds along with its food. The amount would be too little to cause any harm, but the substance would remain in its body. A bird feeding on worms would eat not one worm, but many of them. With each worm the bird would consume a little of the substance. It would still be too little to cause any injury, but its body would accumulate the compound from all the worms it had eaten.

After one meal, as the bird flew away, it might be caught and eaten by a hawk. The hawk would eat many small birds, accumulating in its body the compound from all the birds it ate. Now the amount in the body of the hawk would be significant. Perhaps—and this is what happened in the case of some organochlorine insecticides—it might affect not the bird itself, but the eggs it laid. These might be less likely to

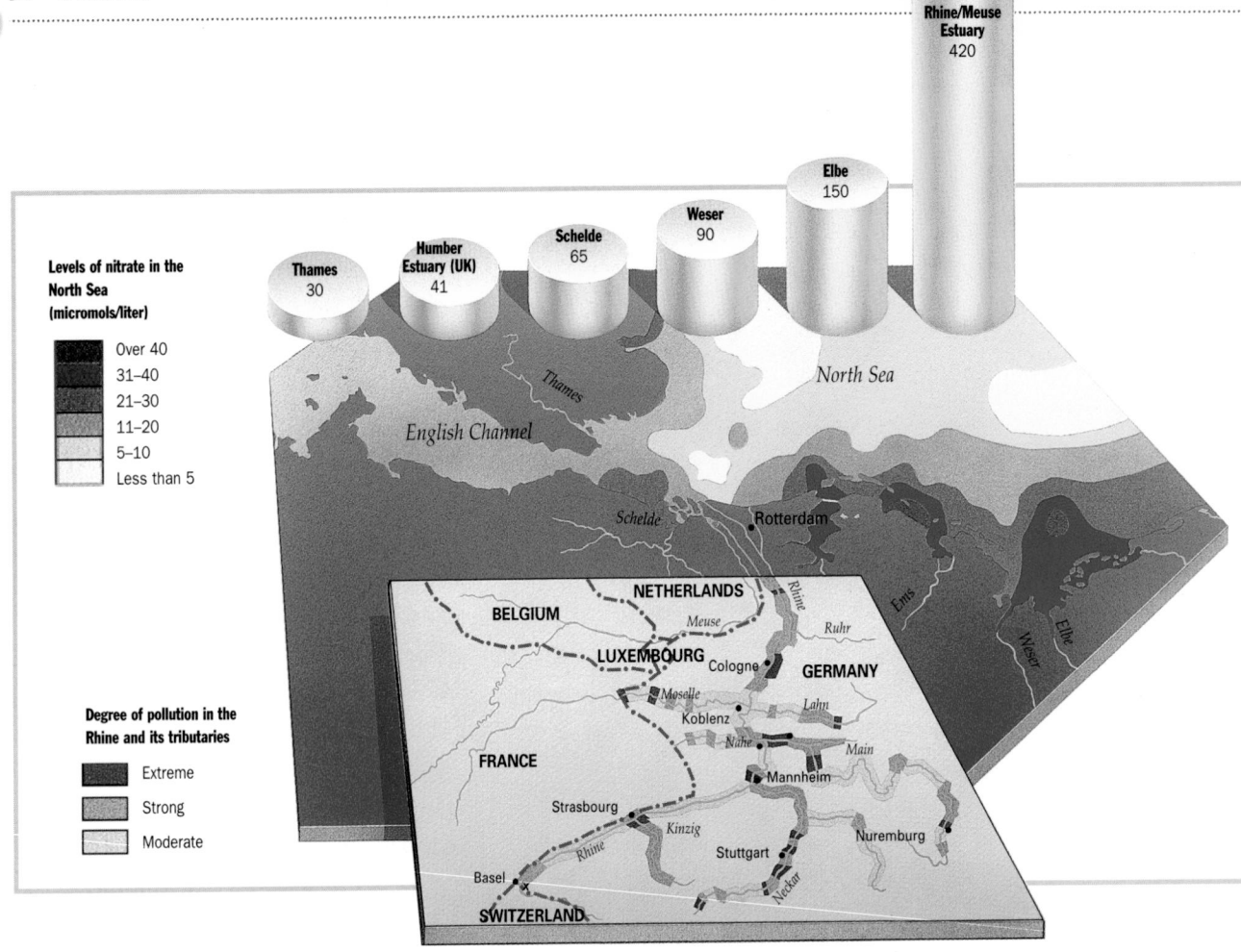

Levels of nitrate in the North Sea (micromols/liter)

- Over 40
- 31–40
- 21–30
- 11–20
- 5–10
- Less than 5

Degree of pollution in the Rhine and its tributaries

- Extreme
- Strong
- Moderate

Thames 30

Humber Estuary (UK) 41

Schelde 65

Weser 90

Elbe 150

Rhine/Meuse Estuary 420

North Sea

English Channel

Thames

Schelde

Rotterdam

NETHERLANDS

BELGIUM

LUXEMBOURG

GERMANY

FRANCE

Meuse

Ruhr

Rhine

Cologne

Moselle

Koblenz

Lahn

Nahe

Main

Mannheim

Strasbourg

Kinzig

Stuttgart

Nuremburg

Basel

Neckar

SWITZERLAND

Ems

Weser

Elbe

POLLUTION ON THE RHINE. The Rhine carries water drained from the industrial heartland of northwestern European cities into the North Sea.

hatch or might have unusually thin shells that broke easily.

The chain leading from worm to small bird to hawk is called a food chain. There are substances that can accumulate along food chains until they reach concentrations high enough to cause harm. This is called biological amplification or biomagnification. Companies are no longer allowed to sell substances that could lead to biological amplification. Pesticides (chemicals used to poison insect and other pests and weeds) are subjected to tight controls.

Coastal Pollution

Rivers flow into the sea, and if the rivers are polluted, the pollutants they carry also enter the

sea. There, they may be diluted, but in small seas they can cause serious contamination.

The Mediterranean, Adriatic, and Black Seas lose water mainly by evaporation. Pollution from the rivers entering them, including the Ebro, Rhône, Po, Danube, Dniepr, Don, and Nile, accumulate because there is nowhere for them to go. Countries bordering these seas are taking steps to reduce pollution from rivers, but problems remain. From time to time algal blooms kill fish and seaweed, and offshore winds drive rotting vegetation onto the shores of the Adriatic.

The North Sea also receives the discharges from rivers serving major industrial regions of northern Europe. The Rhine, for example, drains land in Switzerland, Austria, France, Germany,

THE LIFE OF THE RIVER THAMES. Improvements in sewage treatment have reduced the level of harmful substances entering London's major river. This has led to a rapid increase since the 1960s in the percentage of dissolved oxygen in the water and the number of fish species living in the river.

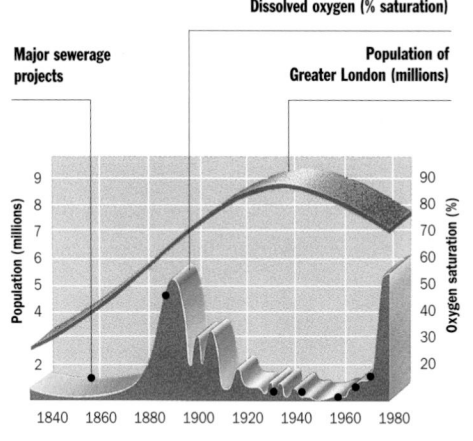

Dissolved oxygen (% saturation)

Major sewerage projects

Population of Greater London (millions)

Luxembourg, Belgium, and the Netherlands and flows through 12 large cities.

Tides in the North Sea cause water to flow counterclockwise in a large circle. River discharges are not carried out into the center of the sea, but move approximately parallel to the coast, traveling from one country to the next.

Marine pollution from rivers can be remedied only by improving the quality of river water. This can be done. The River Thames in London used to be severely polluted with sewage and industrial wastes. Control of discharges into it since the 1960s has led to a marked improvement. Salmon returned to the river some years ago, and more than 100 species of fish now live in the river that not long ago was almost lifeless.

THE RAMSAR CONVENTION

In 1971 an international conference was held in Ramsar, Iran, to devise a way to prevent wetlands from being lost. The result was the Ramsar Convention on Wetlands of International Importance Especially as Waterfowl Habitat.

Under the Ramsar Convention governments designate important wetland areas within their own territories. The eventual aim is to identify a chain of habitats used by migrating birds so they are able to move freely between their feeding and breeding grounds. Designation protects the wetlands from development, and international conservation bodies work in collaboration with the United Nations Environment Program to supervise the working of the convention.

By 1998, 108 governments had signed the convention, and 907 sites had been designated throughout the world.

CYCLE OF AN ALGAL BLOOM. After an algal bloom and the death of the algae the water becomes deoxygenated, causing other animals to die. With offshore winds rotting vegetation and fish are circulated back to the shore. Algal blooms are common in the Adriatic in summer and are unpleasant for people living in coastal areas of Italy and Greece.

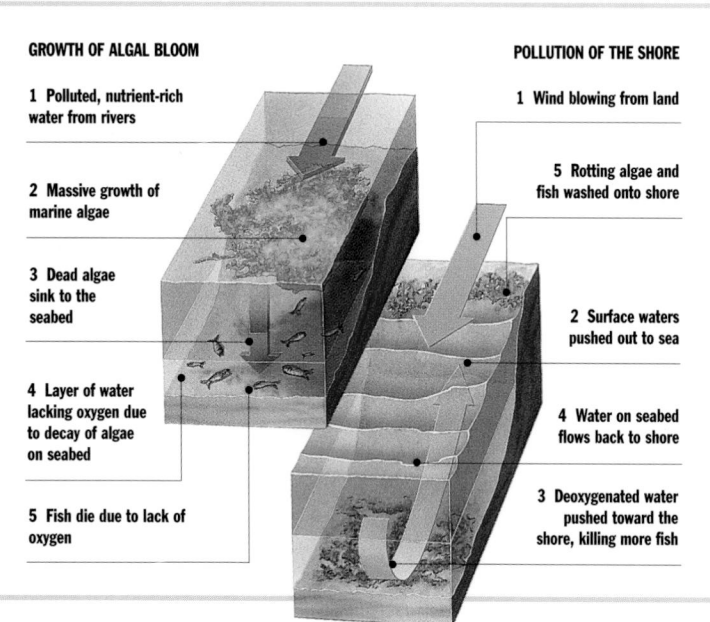

GROWTH OF ALGAL BLOOM

1 Polluted, nutrient-rich water from rivers

2 Massive growth of marine algae

3 Dead algae sink to the seabed

4 Layer of water lacking oxygen due to decay of algae on seabed

5 Fish die due to lack of oxygen

POLLUTION OF THE SHORE

1 Wind blowing from land

5 Rotting algae and fish washed onto shore

2 Surface waters pushed out to sea

4 Water on seabed flows back to shore

3 Deoxygenated water pushed toward the shore, killing more fish

Glossary

aerenchyma Specialized plant tissue in which there are large air spaces that allow air from parts of the plant above the surface to reach parts that are submerged in water.

alga A simple green plant that lacks true leaves, stem, and root. Many algae are single-celled; some are multicelled. Seaweeds are algae.

amphibian A vertebrate animal of the class Amphibia. The young develop in water, although the adults may live on land. Frogs, toads, newts, and salamanders are amphibians.

atoll A circular island, or group of small islands approximately forming a circle; it is formed by a coral reef that has grown around the rim of the crater of a submarine volcano.

bacteria Microscopic organisms, most of which are single-celled, that are found in air, water, and soil everywhere. Different types vary in shape and way of life.

barrier island A long, narrow island lying parallel to a coast that has formed from sand deposited by a current flowing parallel to the shore, or as a ridge exposed by a fall in sea level.

biome A large region throughout which living conditions for plants and animals are broadly similar, so the region can be classified according to its vegetation type.

bog A community of plants living on waterlogged ground in acidic conditions that slow the rate at which organic matter decomposes, causing it to form peat.

brackish Salty, but less so than sea water, having a salt content between 3‰ and 22‰.

buccal respiration Breathing in which the nostrils are closed while air is forced into the lungs by raising the floor of the mouth. Amphibians breathe in this way.

carnivore An animal that feeds exclusively on other animals.

consumer An organism that is unable to manufacture its own food from simple ingredients but must obtain it by eating (consuming) other organisms.

convection Transfer of heat through a liquid or gas by the movement of the liquid or gas.

cutaneous respiration Breathing by absorbing oxygen through the skin. Amphibians absorb a substantial proportion of their oxygen in this way.

cyanobacterium A bacterium that carries out photosynthesis. Cyanobacteria were formerly known as "blue-green algae."

delta A projection of sediment deposited by a large river near its mouth, through which the river may then flow along a number of channels.

ecology The study of the relationships among living organisms in a defined area and between the organisms and the nonliving features of their surroundings.

ecosystem A community of living organisms and their nonliving environment within a defined area. This may be of any size. A forest may be studied as an ecosystem and so may a drop of water.

estuary The region where a river flows into the sea and fresh and salt water meet.

eulittoral zone The lower part of the seashore. It is exposed at low tide.

eutrophic Highly enriched in nutrients.

fen An area of land that is wet for much of the time and is made up largely of peaty soil that is alkaline or neutral (not acid).

flocculation The process by which suspended particles clump together by the attraction of opposite electrical charges and sink to the bottom.

floodplain An area that is periodically flooded by the river flowing across it.

gill 1 The organ with which an aquatic animal obtains oxygen from water. It consists of thin membranes with a large surface area over which water flows. Oxygen passes from the water through the walls of blood vessels in the gill membrane and into the blood. Most aquatic animals have two gills. **2** A bladelike structure in the fruiting body of a fungus (often the visible stage in the life of the fungus, such as a toadstool or mushroom) from which spores are released.

ground water Water below ground that fills all the spaces between soil particles, thus saturating the soil.

halophyte A land plant that tolerates salt and can grow in salt-laden soil or air.

herbivore An animal that feeds exclusively on plants.

holdfast The structure by which an alga, such as a seaweed, is attached to a surface for anchorage. A holdfast may resemble a root, or be disk-shaped and equipped with suckers.

impermeable Restricting or preventing the passage of water.

insectivore An animal that feeds mainly or exclusively on insects.

insectivorous plant A plant, such as a pitcher plant or sundew, that obtains nutrients by trapping and digesting insects. This method of nutrition is an adaptation to life where nutrients are scarce.

invertebrate An animal that does not have a backbone.

lagoon A shallow body of sea water that is partly enclosed by land, restricting its contact with the open sea. Lagoons are enclosed by reefs or islands; the water inside an atoll is a lagoon.

larva An immature form of an animal that is quite different in structure and appearance from the adult but is able to move and feed itself, although usually it is incapable of reproducing.

levee A raised embankment beside a river, made from coarse sediment deposited each time the river overflows. In some cases levees on both banks may allow the river to flow at a level higher than that of the floodplain to either side.

lichen A plantlike organism consisting of a fungus and either an alga or a cyanobacterium living in close association. The visible part of a lichen may be crustlike, scaly, leafy, or shrubby.

littoral Of the shore.

lung The organ of respiration in air-breathing vertebrates. In land-dwelling mollusks (snails and slugs), the part of the body involved in respiration.

mangal A mangrove forest.

mangrove A tree, belonging to one of several species, that grows in mud along tropical coasts and in creeks and estuaries. It has roots that project above the surface to obtain air. These trap sediment, often causing the coast to extend seaward.

marsh An area of more or less permanent wet ground where conditions are not acid.

mesotrophic Having a concentration of nutrients intermediate between those of nutrient-poor (oligotrophic) and nutrient-rich (eutrophic) water.

nymph The immature form of an insect in which the wings develop gradually and there is no pupal stage or rapid metamorphosis. Dragonfly young live as nymphs.

oligotrophic Having few nutrients.

ombrogenous Dependent on rain water for mineral nutrients.

omnivore An animal that eats food derived from both plants and animals.

operculum A small lid, such as that which covers the opening to the gills of a fish and that with which a snail can close its shell.

paedogenesis Reproduction by an animal that is still in its larval stage.

parasite An organism that lives on the surface, or inside the body of, another organism. The parasite is usually smaller than its host and gets food, shelter, or some other necessity from it. The effects of the parasite on its host may range from none at all to severe illness or even death.

photosynthesis The series of chemical reactions by which green plants manufacture sugars, obtaining hydrogen from water and carbon from carbon dioxide, the energy driving the reactions being provided by light that is absorbed by chlorophyll.

phytoplankton *See* plankton.

plankton The small organisms that live near the surface of water and drift with movements of the water. They include single-celled plants (phytoplankton) and small animals (zooplankton), some of which are the larvae of fish and crustaceans.

pneumatophore A "breathing" root found in some plants that grow in waterlogged soil. Part of the root projects above the surface and contains many pores through which gases can be exchanged. These connect with spaces throughout the submerged portion of the root, allowing air to reach all parts.

polder An area of land that has been reclaimed from the sea and is protected from the sea by dikes or embankments.

predator An organism that obtains food by consuming another organism. Most predators are animals that chase, overpower, and kill their prey, but insectivorous plants are also predators.

producer An organism, such as a green plant, that assembles large, complex substances from simple ingredients. These may then be eaten by consumers. On land the principal producers are green plants and in water they are phytoplankton (*see* plankton).

respiration 1 The oxidation of carbon to carbon dioxide in cells with the release of energy. **2** The action of breathing.

salinity A measure of the amount of salt present in water, usually expressed in parts per thousand, symbol ‰. The salinity of sea water varies between 33‰ and 38‰, the average being 35‰.

sublittoral zone The part of the sea shore that extends from the low-tide line seawards to a depth of about 656 feet (200 m) or to the edge of the continental shelf.

supralittoral zone The part of the sea shore that lies above the high-tide line, so it is never submerged, but that is affected by sea spray.

swamp An area of land that lies beneath shallow water throughout the year.

tarn A small upland lake that has no river to carry water away from it, its level being maintained by evaporation. Tarns are usually shallow, although they often have a reputation for being bottomless, due to the lack of any outflow.

transpiration The loss of water vapor through pores, called stomata in the leaves and lenticels in the stems, of green plants.

tropics Those parts of the world that lie between latitudes 23°30'N and 23°30'S. These latitudes mark the boundaries of the region within which the Sun is directly overhead at noon on at least one day each year. The Tropic of Cancer is to the north of the equator and the Tropic of Capricorn to the south.

valve 1 One of the two halves of the shell of some mollusks, such as mussels, scallops, and oysters. **2** The part of the shell of a lampshell (brachiopod) or barnacle that resembles a lid. **3** A flap that can close to allow a fluid to flow in only one direction.

vertebrate An animal that has a backbone. Vertebrates also have a bony skull containing the brain and a skeleton made from bone or cartilage. Fish, amphibians, reptiles, birds, and mammals are vertebrates.

water table The uppermost margin of the ground water, below which the soil is saturated and above which it is not, although it is wet.

yolk A substance, consisting mainly of fats and proteins, that provides nourishment for a growing embryo.

zooplankton *See* plankton.

Further Reading

Basics of Environmental Science by Michael Allaby. Routledge.

Biology by Neil A. Campbell. The Benjamin/Cummings Publishing Co. Inc.

The Encyclopedia of Birds edited by Christopher M. Perrins and Alex L.A. Middleton. Facts on File.

The Encyclopedia of Insects edited by Christopher O'Toole. Facts on File

The Encyclopedia of Mammals edited by David Macdonald. Facts on File

The Encyclopedia of Reptiles and Amphibians edited by Tim Halliday and Kraig Adler. Facts on File.

Flowering Plants of the World edited by V.H. Heywood. Oxford University Press, New York.

Green Planet edited by David M. Moore. Cambridge University Press.

The Hunters by Philip Whitfield. Simon and Schuster.

Hutchinson Encyclopedia of the Earth edited by Peter J. Smith. Hutchinson.

The Lie of the Land edited by K.J. Gregory. Oxford University Press, New York.

Longman Illustrated Animal Encyclopedia edited by Philip Whitfield. Guild Publishing.

The Oxford Encyclopedia of Trees of the World edited by Bayard Hora. Oxford University Press, New York.

Planet Earth: Cosmology, Geology, and the Evolution of Life and Environment by Cesare Emiliani. Cambridge University Press.

Snakes of the World by Chris Mattison. Blandford Press Ltd.

The Science of Ecology by Richard Brewer. Saunders College Publishing, Harcourt Brace College Publishers.

The Encyclopedia of Aquatic Life edited by Keith Banister and Andrew Campbell. Facts on File.

Web site:

The Center for Wetlands, a University of Florida site, devoted mainly to the ecology and management of wetlands, is at: http://www.enveng.ufl.edu/wetlands/

Photographic Acknowledgments

7 C.J. Lenars/Explorer; **10** Powerstock/Zefa Photo Library; **12–13, 14–15** A.G.E. Fotostock/Images Colour Library; **19** Heather Angel/Biofotos; **21** Ronald Thompson/Frank W. Lane/Bruce Coleman Limited; **24** Bomford & Borkowski/Ardea London; **27** E. Murtomäki/Natural History Photographic Agency; **32** Bob Gibbons; **34–35** Lee/Picture Box/Natural History Photographic Agency; **37** Udo Hirsch/Bruce Coleman Limited; **40** David Wright/Oxford Scientific Films; **49** S. Osolinski/Oxford Scientific Films; **Cover pictures:** *top:* Fritz Prenzel/Bruce Coleman Limited; *bottom:* David Hughes/Bruce Coleman Limited; *globe motif:* Terra Forma™ Copyright© 1995–1997 Andromeda Interactive Ltd.

Set Index

Page numbers in *italics*
refer to illustrations; volume
numbers are in **bold**.